D1571660

"An urgent and useful guide for a... ... ... make a difference. It will change your work for the better."
— *Seth Godin, Author, This Is Marketing*

"If you want to change the world, not just talk about it, but actually change it, *read this book.*"
— *Jesse Schell, Distinguished Professor of Entertainment Technology, Carnegie Mellon University; Author, The Art of Game Design @jesseschell*

"During this era of massive environmental, technological, and sociopolitical change, Katie is a beacon of optimism and hope about humans' capacity to heal the biosphere and earth system. She brings great enthusiasm, wisdom, and clarity in identifying several concrete steps each of us can take to sustain our local and global surroundings. This book is creative, informative, beautifully illustrated, and user-friendly. Katie has written a truly valuable and timely guide to the dilemmas we're facing in the early 21st Century and the behaviors we can enact to help heal and sustain the world."
— *Dan Stokols, Chancellor's Professor Emeritus, School of Social Ecology, University of California, Irvine; Author, Social Ecology in the Digital Age @dstokols*

"*How to Save the World* is invaluable for change-makers looking to make real impact in communities through the use of government data. One cannot go through any of the steps in this book without figuring out how to use civic data for doing good, and that's a frontier all innovators, journalists and startup founders should be very excited about."
— *Jay Nath, Co-Executive Director, City Innovate; former Chief Innovation Officer, City of San Francisco @Jay_Nath*

"Katie has delivered what we in the change movement have needed for a long time—a pragmatic, fun, and smart guide to making your positive impact on the world really happen."
— *Aaron Hurst, Co-Founder & CEO, Imperative; Author, The Purpose Economy; Founder, The Taproot Foundation @Aaron_Hurst*

"I've always loved Katie's enthusiasm. She is one of my engineering heroes and has grown to become a true force for change. This remarkable book continues Katie's amazing journey. It is easy to read, practical and full of ways for you to act, and help us survive in a world where the evidence of climate change and sustainability collapse can be frightening, and even bring on despair. But, as Al Gore told us 'A lot of people go straight from denial to despair without pausing in the middle and doing something about it.' Katie's enthusiasm shines from every page, and fires hope for my grandchildren. I urge all to read this book, to 'think beautifully,' and get out there and do epic things to save the world. Never has this call to *action* been more damn serious."
— *Professor David A Hood, AM HonFIEAust; Chairman, The Long Future Foundation; 2012 National President Engineers Aus. @davidahood43*

"Katie Patrick's new book *How to Save the World* does a wonderful job of explaining how creativity can be applied to the global challenges we and the earth face. Her vision and advice have the power to lead to profound positive change. Highly recommended!"
— *Eric Maisel Ph.D., Author, Coaching the Artist Within @ericmaisel*

"Maximizing measurable impact is one of the most important frontiers in the social impact profession right now, and *How to Save the World* presents a detailed and well-thought-out process to follow to achieve that. This book is an important and timely resource for anyone wanting to do less talking about change, and make real impact in the world."
— *Dr James Gifford, Research Fellow, University of Zurich; Founding Executive Director, UN Principles for Responsible Investment*

"Katie has articulated an important call to arms to infuse the critical skills of creativity, optimism, and imagination into the realm of environmental change. This books is a great asset to anyone wanting to change the world, because the practice of positive imagination is one of the most important ingredients in changing the world for the better."
— *Scott Barry Kaufman Ph.D., Author, Wired to Create; Professor, Columbia University @sbkaufman*

"Katie's book on approaching the sometimes fraught topic of global environmental change and the actions that can help save the world is exactly what 'change wanters' should read! By presenting the state of knowledge in what actually works, in a way that we can all understand, using beautiful and simple graphics, Katie has delivered something useful for all walks of life, from all corners of the world."
— *Jeremy Hoffman, Ph.D., Climate & Earth Scientist, The Science Museum of Virginia @jer_science*

"Very insightful and thought-provoking. Great presentation style. I especially appreciated the idea that sustainable change requires us to establish a metric for progress toward that change."
— *Jim Cybulski Ph.D., CEO & Founder, Foldscope Instruments @TeamFoldscope*

"*Save the world?* This is exactly the kind of optimistic vision we need most right now. This book lays out practical and inspired ways to train yourself to make your good ideas bear fruit. Whether you're just starting out in your world-saving venture, or if you're an old hand looking to recharge and learn new techniques, this book is for you."
— *Nick Aster, Founder, TriplePundit.com @nickaster*

"This is a very well-thought-out, detailed presentation of the material. My sense of digital design is far from sophisticated and I was extremely impressed to see the many ways that data visualization may be brought to bear on environmental and other sorts of information that I was not aware of. Strongly recommended."
— *Rebecca Skinner Ph.D., Founder, Urban Dashboard Air Monitoring @UrbanDashboard*

"*How to Save the World* provides a brilliant framework for creative people, like myself, to connect our work with making a measurable impact. This book is a fantastic introduction, filled with unique insights and case studies, for anybody that is seriously interested in how to make the world a better place. I was skeptical that a single book could deliver such a bold promise, but since reading, I'm a convert! "
— *Benjamin Von Wong, Artist, Guinness World Record Winner #Strawpocalypse @thevonwong*

"Katie's book *How to Save the World* translates cutting edge behavioral research into a straightforward method to create campaigns of change. Those who would like to effectively wield social science to meet our environmental challenges should read this book."
— *Gregg Sparkman Ph.D., Environmental Social Scientist, Stanford University*

HOW TO SAVE THE WORLD

How to make changing the world the
greatest game we've ever played

Katie Patrick

Published by Hello World Labs
San Francisco

How to Save the World
is published by
Hello World Labs
1086 Folsom Street
San Francisco
California 94103

Edited by: Conna Craig (connacraig@gmail.com) and Eva Rottenanger (evamurray81@gmail.com).

This book is carbon neutral with carbon credits from Carbonfund.org and is printed on partially recycled paper that is Forest Stewardship Certified. Printing process is ISO 140001 environmental certified.

For workshops, speaking, design, and software development inquiries, email Katie at kp@helloworlde.com and learn more about Hello World Labs in San Francisco at helloworlde.com. Join Katie's global community of world-changers at katiepatrick.com and subscribe to the *How to Save the World* podcast on Itunes.

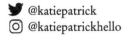 @katiepatrick
@katiepatrickhello

For the beautiful Anastasia Violet
and for all my friends who dream of a better world.

I dedicate this book to that little seed inside every one of you that yearns for meaning, that craves to push boundaries, and that delights in making beautiful things.

This book is for all of you who try to hold the expanding universe in each blink of your consciousness, and actually believe that your dreams of how beautiful the world *could* become will one day come true.

CONTENTS

Welcome, Friend 4

The Biggest Mistake 8

Call to Adventure 18

Your Creative Genius Zone 26

How I Got Here 40

Step 1: Measure It 50

Step 2: The Goal 82

Step 3: Visualize Your World 88

Step 4: Idea Storm 100

Step 5: Idea Evaluation 112

Step 6: Behavior Change 120

Step 7: Systems Thinking 148

Step 8a: Game Design 160

Step 8b: Tell Your Story 212

Step 9: Tribes & Tipping Points 224

Step 10: Technology 240

In Summary Diagram 249

It's the End, But It's Really the Beginning 252

Wonder

My intention is that this book inspires a never-ending sense of *wonder* in the process of creating the amazing, interesting, inspiring, colorful, fun, and *effective* ways you can save the Earth, and how you can discover your own enlightenment and joy that comes when you get it *right*.

WELCOME, FRIEND

You're here because you want to do something amazing.

You're a budding entrepreneur. You're an activist. You're a thinker. You want to change the world. You want to solve real problems—interesting problems. Most of all you just want to *do things that matter.*

There are a lot of books that teach you how to do things. They have titles like *How to Start a Business*, or *How to Run Your First Marathon*. There is at least one "how to" methodology for pretty much anything anyone might possibly ever want to do. But the art of saving the world is a reasonably new domain. We haven't really had a "how to" methodology to follow, and there aren't many books that are designed to teach you the very critical things you need to know to take on big-deal challenges like, for example, changing a whole civilization.

Seminal works like Al Gore's *An Inconvenient Truth*, Amory Lovin's *Natural Capitalism,* and more recently Paul Hawkin's *Drawdown* powerfully illustrate the problems of our time, and also teach practical solutions to these problems, such as closing down the world's coal power stations, eating less meat, or covering millions of rooftops with solar panels. Whether you're sitting at your desk in the morning, shocked about another melted glacier, or you're walking through an aromatic forest feeling inspired about your next social-change mission—what do you *actually do* next? Where do you start? How do you turn the embryo of an idea or a dream into a *movement*? How do you get thousands or even millions of inspired citizens to roll out these changes in the cities across the world? How do you tackle the infinitely complex job of making *real and measurable change*?

Throughout my twenty-year career in sustainability, I finally started to notice that while there's a great deal of information about *what* we need to do to change the world, we've been mostly in the dark on *how* to actually bring about the change we desire. We need to add something else that focused on the "how" to turn so many important solutions from ideas into reality. To do this, we must dig deeply into a missing piece that's been too often left out of the picture: the psychology of human influence.

Many people work passionately on the causes they care about. But they are also prone to making big mistakes that result in a whole lot of effort being expended and never seeing a whole lot of change. When you are putting lots of hours and energy into a cause, it's easy to live in an illusion that your efforts are making change happen, when in fact there is very little evidence to suggest it. I used to be one of those people myself.

With an obsession to crack the code on what makes change happen, I've studied far and wide for many years, well outside the boundaries of my trade in traditional environmental engineering. I've studied game design, lived in Silicon Valley hacker houses, learned about behavioral psychology practiced user interface design, read up on systems theory, learned to code, practiced soldering electronics, and hunted through academic journals for the gems of knowledge that will help us pull out the bricks in the wall that we have so often bashed our heads against. I wrote this manual for you my friend, to be your ultimate "how to" guide.

There is a science and a methodology to changing the world. This book will help you apply a structured design process to the difficult job of untangling solutions to these very hard problems we work on so that you can experience the joy of actually creating *real and measurable change.*

We're currently experiencing the greatest shift we've ever seen in the strategic approach it takes to change the world. That's because the world is being covered in electronic sensors that are acting like a distributed network of digital eyes and ears, letting us see deeply into issues that we could not see before. In this new age, drones are tracking endangered species, air quality sensors are mapping polluted city streets, and satellites are sending images of illegal deforestation within a few hours of it happening. There are thousands of new applications of technology delivering an explosion of data about the biggest environmental trends of our time.

In addition to this technology boom, we're quickly learning more about the psychology of behavior, motivation, and human happiness. The rapid advance of data science and psychology, have opened up a whole new age of social-change innovation that just hasn't been available to us before. It's exciting stuff! This means that the old style of changing the world is ending and a new age is dawning. Gone are the days of depressing scare campaigns, eco-guilt marketing, and those *oh-so-tedious* conferences. We are entering a new age, where social and environmental change projects are data-driven, high-tech, and optimized for resonance with the human mind.

But the most exciting part is that there are incredible new ideas, breakthroughs, and history-changing moments all over the world just waiting to hatch. While the techniques you'll read about in this book have been proven to yield big results, many of them have not yet been implemented in the real world in a big way. The ten steps, case studies, and tutorials in this book will guide you through a design process that will help you uncover new ideas as if they were little Easter eggs in the grass just waiting for you to find them.

People sometimes ask me if I get depressed or overwhelmed by focusing my life on environmental problems. This is the thing—my consciousness does not linger in the problems of the world. My daily thoughts are immersed in the process of creating solutions that are *building a new world*, and now I'm ever-more confident that I'm starting to understand how it needs to be done. Every day I get to work on creating software, videos, books, presentations, and games that are fun and motivating. Every day I occupy a realm of the imagination that involves carefully visualizing the incredible future we are creating. Every day (well, *almost* every day), I'm eager, full of ideas, and inspired.

So what do I mean by "Save the World"? It's a fun title from the '80s when I first got into environmentalism, from the days of hand-drawn Earth and peace signs that said "Save the World!" and adorned t-shirts and bumper stickers and canvas bags. It wasn't a cliché then. The title of this book is a tribute to the beginning of the movement. It sounds fun and bombastic, and I like that.

But the serious definition of "how to save the world" is to take an idea or intention for how you want to *improve* the world, and turn it into a project that makes measurable social or environmental change. It could be an idea to reach renewable energy that you turn it into thousands of solar panels installed. It could be starting with an idea to get kids to grow food at schools and turning it into real food gardens in 100 schools in your state. It could be an idea to get off gas cars that leads to a 50 percent reduction in gas car ownership in your city. While lots of ideas get stuck in the mental cloud of an idea, or a blog post, saving the world, means being able to hold up a number at the end of the day that quantifies what you actually saved.

Saving the world must never be a dreary task. It is an infinite pool of the greatest wealth that life has to offer: a wealth of purpose, of fascinating problem solving, and of taking your place in the greatest chess game there ever was. In the words of John F. Kennedy, *"We choose to go to the moon in this decade and do the other [scientific] things, not because they are easy, but because they are hard, because that goal will serve to organize and measure the best of our energies and skills, because that challenge is one that we are willing to accept, one we are unwilling to postpone, and one which we intend to win . . ."* If these problems weren't difficult to solve, they would have already been fixed. That's what makes saving the world the most exciting and stimulating profession on Earth, and the greatest challenge that ever was. It's a tantalizing adventure, and I truly believe it is the greatest game we've ever played.

I hope this book will inspire you to grow into your wildest creative dreams for what the world *could* be, and be filled with the wonder that guides us to push boundaries in science, technology, art, and the human spirit to get us there.

The core theme that threads through the ten steps in this book is bringing the measurement of what you want to change to the center of the creative process. As this lens comes into focus, I think you'll discover some big new ideas that are ready to hatch, and maybe even a little magic in you. When we learn to master the evidence-based techniques that are proven to create measurable change, we *really can change the world*. No matter what a cliché it has become, changing the world is a truly awesome way to spend your life.

So why not get really good at it? Let's begin our journey deep into the game. We'll be playing for the most epic win of all.

THE BIGGEST MISTAKE

"Whatever you think you can do or believe you can do, begin it. Action has magic, grace and power in it." — Johann Wolfgang von Goethe

If you have a job, campaign, project, or a startup where your role is to make change happen and influence people for the better, then it's likely that you have fallen prey to one of the most prevalent, yet hardly known mistakes that thousands of nonprofits, governments, and activists have made before you. I call it "The Biggest Mistake" and it starts with an innocent and seemingly logical hypothesis: that *knowing* about a thing motivates people to *do* a thing.

For a long time, people made the assumption that if they simply *educated* others about the big issues they cared about, then other people would care about these issues, too. They assumed that instilling a new-found knowledge and emotional concern in others would motivate concerned citizens to do the things that would drive a landslide of change. Most people who are trying to change the world think that *educating* people on issues leads to people making changes in their *actions*. It's an easy mistake to make, but the hypothesis is wrong. Let me explain.

Mistake 1:
The Value-Action Gap

This pesky problem which crops up whenever we try to get people to change is called *The Value-Action Gap*. It means that there is very little relationship between educating people on an issue and how that education leads people to engage in behaviors or actions that support your cause.(1) This phenomenon is easy for behavioral scientists to test. One simple experiment involves getting a group of students to watch a documentary or attend a class about energy efficiency and climate change. When the students are asked about how they *feel* about the issue, they claim to be concerned about climate change. The educational efforts *are* effective in eliciting emotional concern. But when the students were observed for any change in their behavior that would save energy, such as switching off lights, using heaters less, or closing windows, there was no observable effect whatsoever. (2) No one *actually did anything.*

The same phenomenon is seen in purchasing of ethical or sustainable items. Just because someone is concerned or educated about an issue like fair trade wages or pesticides used on cotton, this bears little impact on any lifestyle change, purchasing choice, or civic action that person might engage in.(3,4) It's because the intellectual exercise of learning something about the world isn't a direct door into the gearbox that governs human behavior.

It's easy to presume there is a natural connection between a person learning about a serious issue and then taking action on that issue. It's called the *Information Deficit Hypothesis.* You'd think that giving people information can turn a light bulb on in their mind and that their actions are forever guided toward the light to do more good things. *But no cigar.* This doesn't mean that education is not important in a social change campaign. Education *is* important. But your campaign needs to be targeted primarily to promoting *a specific behavior or action.*

It's quite possible that almost every booklet, documentary, lecture, advertising

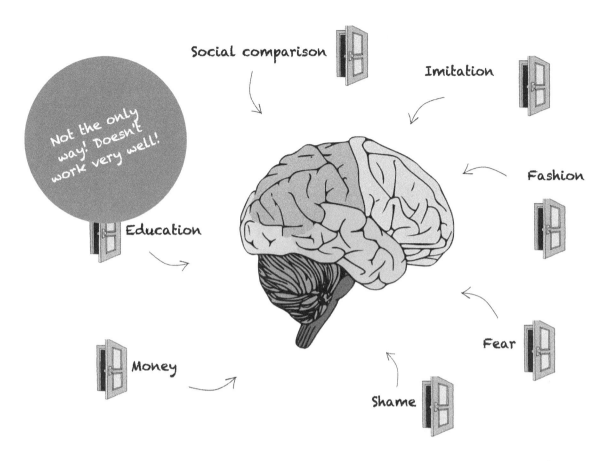

Doors to the motivational core: some doors are ineffective at influencing people, while others are highly effective. Providing educational material is one of the lesser effective ways to influence people to change.

campaign, conference, festival, and magazine ever produced in the hope of changing the world has fallen, at least in part, down into the crevasse of the Value-Action Gap. It doesn't mean that these educational mediums should be abandoned, but they do need to be strategically positioned as one puzzle piece in a larger jigsaw of *behavior design*. The master key to bridging the gap starts with this understanding: a *behavior* campaign is an entirely different beast than an *education* campaign. We don't need to educate people in order to change the world, but we do need to get people to change their actions and their habits.

Think of the human psyche as a house with a motivational core that sits at the center like a glowing warm fireplace. There are several doors you can enter to get to that core. Education is one door, but it's not a direct one. When you enter it, it leads you around the corridor and back outside. Some doors will take you up the stairs to the attic, some to the basement. Some doors are locked completely. When

THE EDUCATION APPROACH VS

Let's look at an example of a project to get people in a large office building to use fewer disposable plastic bottles. If we make the mistake of thinking that *education* leads to change, we might design an *educational* strategy like this:

1. Putting up a poster that has facts about plastic waste in the lunchroom.

2. Getting a local environmental leader to give a talk about plastic pollution.

3. Putting a pamphlet on reducing plastic on every employee's desk.

4. Going to a conference about plastic pollution.

5. Making everyone watch a documentary on how bad plastic is for the environment.

6. Writing a post on the company blog about how the company is trying to reduce its plastic use.

The Value-Action Gap theory indicates that these six educational initiatives will have a weak effect on getting people to change their plastic bottle use. Getting people to *care* about the issue isn't the most important thing in creating change.

THE BEHAVIOR APPROACH

Your project will take a different form when you design it to empower a *behavior*. People already know that disposable plastic is bad. They probably don't need much more education or emotional persuasion. A campaign that targets *behavior* might include:

1. Giving everyone in the office a reusable water bottle.

2. Installing a SodaStream in the office kitchen.

3. Getting each person to write out a pledge to promise to use their reusable water bottle.

4. Adding a smiley face or sad face to the daily chart when re-usable water bottle use goes up or down.

5. Putting up all the written pledges on a wall where people can see them.

6. Installing filtered water refill stations in easy-to-find places.

7. Counting the plastic bottles thrown out every day and writing the number on the wall in a clearly visible place, and charting the numbers over time.

8. Creating a sticker chart and putting a happy sticker on it for each person who uses a reusable plastic water bottle.

People need to feel *empowered* to influence change, like *their one action is making a difference.* These eight techniques empower our group of people *for action.*

you approach a problem by trying to educate people or raise awareness, there's a chance that some people will make it around the corridor, through the window, and down from the attic, but why put people through a psychological labyrinth to get them to make a change? Our job is to understand the blueprint of the human psyche and design a clear entrance, based on the house's architecture, and lead people directly to the inner fireplace of the mind that causes *action*. The ten steps we're going to go through in this book will guide you to develop a concept or project that will bridge the Value-Action Gap.

Mistake 2:
Effort vs Results

There's another mistake that people make when evaluating their involvement in a cause. People confuse the *effort* they put in with the actual impact they are making on the world that is measurable with a number. It goes something like this, *"I've been attending events, talking about this issue to everyone, posting about it on Facebook. I wrote a blog post about it. I painted a banner for the annual protest. I wear a T-shirt about it and read everything I can on the issue."* This person is clearly engaged, and putting in regular hours of work trying to change the world. But let's not confuse all of this effort with *results*.

Imagine a group of people at a school who start a committee to reduce waste, but never consider how to measure how much waste the school creates, or what the waste is made up of. They might design and distribute an educational flyer to students and staff. Over years, the committee will keep on meeting, keep holding workshops, and keep making flyers, which have little or no measurable effect on the amount of waste the school creates. This committee may well live in an illusion that because they are putting *effort* into the cause, the effort is a result in itself. It is not.

The key question to ask is, *"Where is the evidence that your efforts have made a measurable result?"* Ask it of yourself and of any social change project in which you are involved. When we're trying to change the world, all that matters is that we make an impact that is measurable, not in clicks, meetings, or shares, but in real-world data.

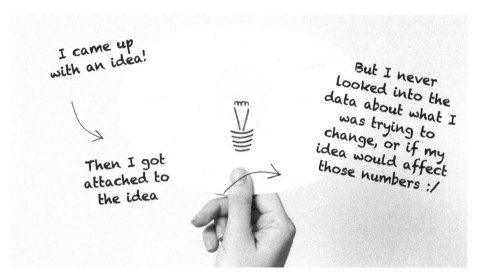

Ideas before the data: Don't make the mistake of coming up with an idea, and getting attached to an idea, before thoroughly investigating the data about your cause.

Mistake 3:
Ideas first, data second

It's common for people to come up with an idea *before* they investigate the data about their cause. A studio comes with an idea for a game to stop climate change, without looking into the data about the many places carbon dioxide emissions come from. A couple comes up with an idea for an app to stop food waste, without studying the numbers on where the food waste occurs. An artist starts work on an idea for an art photography project about marine pollution without studying any research papers about the quantity of plastic in the ocean. Don't do this.

The problem with coming up with ideas before you research your data is that it's possible that the ideas you come up with might have a minimal effect on creating measurable change. You can also become emotionally attached to a not-so-good idea, making it hard to pivot to a better idea that really *will* work to shift the numbers. Failing to take a deep dive into the data first, robs you of profound insights you would not have thought of otherwise. Data will unleash your creativity and help you uncover those *extra special* ideas that will really push the impact you can have. If you've already been working on an idea you came up with before deeply investigating your data (don't worry, everybody has done it!) take a step back and do more research on the numbers. Our first chapter on measurement will get to the heart of this issue and get you started on the right track.

How do you avoid making these all-too-common mistakes? The first step is to divide your cause into the two lenses of *measurement* and *behavior*. All problems are *measurable*. All solutions require a *human behavior*.

Measurement

The first step is to measure in detail what you want to change in the world. Use these numbers as the skeleton of your creative strategy.

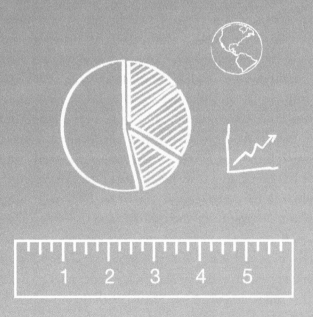

The art of making change involves
developing a project that gets humans to
do things that make measurable change.

Second lens

Behavior

The second step is to identify the behavior or action you
want people to take in the real world. All change
requires a human to *do a thing*.

CALL TO ADVENTURE

"The future belongs to those who believe in the beauty of their dreams."
— Eleanor Roosevelt, First Lady of the United States

The task of saving the world is not about languishing in the badlands of ineffective activism. It is a truly *great adventure*. It is an adventure into inventing new ways of doing just about everything, exploring uncharted realms of the imagination, and in the words of Star Trek's famous acclamation, *"To go where no one has gone before."* As you start using this book to design your rocket ship of world-changing strategies, you will be embarking on an adventure into a new world. You need a whole lot of fuel to get there. The fuel that will propel your rocket ship into the world-changing stratosphere is *a dream*—a dream of what this new world you are creating will look, function, and feel like.

Wooden Orchids by Vincent Callebaut Architectures.

I'll share my dream with you. I go through life seeing two worlds: the regular world I can see with my eyes, and this other world I can see in my mind. In my mind, I can see a world that is truly extraordinary: vibrant with human energy, beautiful by design, and built with deep ecological intelligence. This vision is almost like a mental transparency or an animation that layers over the top of the real world. I see our potential as a civilization to evolve into the better part of ourselves where we live in a state of extraordinary empathy, intelligence, and love.

As a young environmental engineer, I started to piece together an incredible vision for the future of humanity—a future where we had left behind the crude kind of engineering that destroys, wastes, and pollutes. The age of ecological destruction had ended and our civilization had graduated into an enlightened high-tech eco-utopia where we had achieved a true symbiotic equilibrium with nature. Our technology and infrastructure had dramatically evolved to be modeled *upon* the intelligence of ecosystems, rather than at the *expense* of them. It was the most beautiful vision I'd ever seen.

To this day, I believe this future to be real. The deeper I get into the game of change, the more evidence I see of this future sprouting up all around me. Do you have a dream also? Do you have a dream for how the world will work when the problems you most care about are solved? Maybe you even have a dream for what the most mind-opening, futuristic, and enlightened future world would look like. Albert Einstein once said *"Imagination is everything. It is the preview to life's*

The Dragonly: Building design inspired by a leaf, by Vincent Callebaut Architectures.

coming attractions." This dream you have is a window into the future you are creating, not only for the world, but for the person *you* become in the process of making it.

Let me share a call to adventure for this new world we are creating. Consider a moment in the future when the last coal power station has been closed and the last gasoline refinery has been decommissioned. Imagine the day when we watch the sun set on the age of fossil fuels and the dawn of a new planet that is entirely solar powered. Imagine the day when we remove the vast amounts of plastic that litters the ocean, washes up on beach shores, and fills the stomachs of marine life, and turn the ocean into a glistening crystal blue sea that is completely plastic-free once again. We stop the ghastly practice of filling gargantuan-sized landfills with mountains of disposable trash. In this future, we have learned how to make the things we need, and the food we eat, with packaging and materials that are reused and composted, so that not only the practice, but the *entire concept* of trash, is all but forgotten.

Imagine living in a new moral universe where widespread consideration for animals has brought the heart-breaking torture that is practiced in animal agriculture to an end. Just as the once commonplace practice of slavery fell (mostly) to the ghosts of history, it is no longer a moral norm to hurt animals for food. Instead, we treat our vertebrate friends with dignity and respect.

Picture a new urban landscape where we turn concrete jungles into living eco-

The explosion of affordable sensor technology, wifi networks, and digital screens is enabling a whole new age of earth intelligence to open up. We can use the same approach that a Fitbit uses to track your steps, but for planet Earth, where we measure the water, the air, and the Earth's whole biosphere. We're experiencing the dawn of a new age of the cybernetic Earth.

cities that are connected by vibrant green roofs and threaded with living wildlife corridors. City buildings are draped in flowering gardens, and suburbs are patch-worked with fertile urban orchards. Think of a city where we can create buildings that are designed to mimic living organisms, like the one in the image called *The Dragonfly,* whose engineering is modeled on the inner workings of a leaf. Imagine we turn around the age of relentlessly devastating deforestation to a new era in which our most precious rainforests are protected and left to fulfill their role as the lungs of the earth. If you believe in the power of creating beautiful things, this dream is our future.

The Cybernetic Earth

There is a new phenomenon spreading across the world that will help make this vision possible. The explosion of affordable sensor technology, wifi networks, and digital screens is enabling a new age of earth intelligence to open up. We can use the same approach that a Fitbit uses to track your steps—but we measure the water, the air, and the Earth's whole biosphere. You could say that we are in the midst of creating a cybernetic Earth: using technology to deeply understand the heartbeat of the planet and giving us the information instantly, so that we can do something about it.

Think of it like this: what would it look like if you could monitor the Earth as if it were a patient in a hospital? When doctors want to know what is going on inside the body of a human patient, they cover the patient in sensors that measure things like heart rate, blood oxygen levels, and brain activity. The doctors can see the information picked up by these sensors on a screen that updates instantly. Doctors know what is going *immediately* because medical devices notify them with a sudden beep and flash of light when something is wrong. If we can care for a human patient in a hospital to such detail, why can't we do this for our planet? *We can.*

When we understand the Earth's biosphere immediately, intimately and quantitatively, then we can better care for the Earth with the responsive detail and deep intelligence the planet needs. It's a vision shared by one of the founders of Google Earth Outreach, Rebecca Moore, *"Well, you really want to know what our dream is? Where everyone can know, using analysis on real-time data coming out of Earth Engine . . . like a living, breathing dashboard for the planet. You can really be tuned into what's happening now."* With deep insight into the workings of the biosphere, we'll be empowered to turn the dream for this new Earth into a tangible reality in our lifetime.

The new and hyper-detailed earth data that is coming online opens up a whole

Illustration of Lebanon covered in treed roofs, by StudioInvisible.

host of social change strategies that simply aren't available without it—we can add colors to easily communicate different grades of air quality, compare one school's monthly garbage to another's, and show our carbon emissions big and bright on beautifully designed digital screens in the heart of the city. Throughout this book, you'll learn more design and behavior-change techniques that you can apply in this new age of data.

Stepping into the next age

We don't have to let our time on Earth be defined by dirty concrete, climate catastrophe, and ecological collapse. We can step into a new era for humankind: the dawn of *the great sustainability enlightenment,* where we carefully tend to our planet and build technology that grows in an interdependent symbiosis with nature.

Saving the world isn't just about stopping bad things and putting out fires. It's about clearing up the mess on the planet *in order for* our next age to take root. In the same way that a clean water supply enables children to go to school instead of walking five hours per day to get water from a well, the global sustainability revolution is building the backbone that will enable humanity to take its next great leap.

City of Waves by Architect Luc Schuiten.

Who will we become, as people, when we're not expending our time and intellect scouring the Earth for the last oil reserves? Or when we're not making plastic bags in a factory every day? Who will we become when we're not spiritually dying in a dead-end office? Or gutting animals in an abattoir? What type of people can we grow into when we've solved the issues of domestic violence and human trafficking? What will our children design when we've weeded out another generation of problems in order to open up the fertile foundations for them to flower?

My parents' generation cleared the way for me to do incredible things with my life, such as studying engineering without a second thought about my gender or learning to code for free from web-streamed video. In my lifetime I will break down walls, invent new machines, and push at the boundaries that will open up a new playing field for my daughter to go farther than I could have ever dreamed for her. You will do the same, and the people who come after you will lean against your progress.

Let's all dream big and beautiful. Our dreams will become real one day. Each one of us can take our place in helping humanity reach our greatest chapter yet.

GENIUS INSIDE

YOUR CREATIVE GENIUS ZONE

"There is a vitality, a life force, an energy, a quickening that is translated through you into action, and because there is only one of you in all of time, this expression is unique. And if you block it, it will never exist through any other medium and it will be lost." — Martha Graham, iconic dancer

Do you ever get a weird feeling like, *there's got to be more to life that this?* Have you ever felt like you had a special kind of skill, or a calling, or some bigger reason for existing? I've had this feeling forever. I think you probably have it, too. I believe this feeling is whispering to you that you are not yet operating from your *creative genius zone* and that you really need to be.

What does your creative genius zone have to do with saving the world? Everything, my friend. One main feature of creative work is that it involves making something that has not been made before. If you want to abolish air pollution, cover your city in green roofs, or get preschoolers to grow their own vegetables, you are going to have to come up with solutions and ideas that *have never been done before*. It is going to take epic imagination, big inspiration, and momentous creativity to come up with the ideas, innovations and social movements that will solve the world's many crises.

The world's problems will not be solved by fighting an enemy, forcing a movement, or sacrificing your own happiness. You need to dig deep into your own creative genius to come up with the ideas we will need to build a new world. This issue is so dear to my heart that I'm ready to scream from any rooftop, anywhere, *that creativity is the only limiting factor in saving the world.*

There's no need to draw your motivation from any sadness caused by the environmental destruction or human suffering you've seen. Be motivated instead by a positive vision of *how beautiful* you think the world *could* be. Your devotion to a cause should not be a sacrifice. It should be your greatest work of art. Do it because the art of designing a sustainable earth is the most beautiful, complex, and enriching craft that you could ever devote your life to mastering.

The Creative Continuum

Creativity can sometimes get typecast as gentle hobbies, like watercolor painting on weekends, or embroidering pillows. I have a deeper philosophy of what creativity is all about, and I think it's much bigger and more fundamental to our time here on Earth that we realize. I think it's even embedded in the nature of the very atoms that make us up.

Working at the coal face of difficult world problems can be challenging, and so it's important for us to get a bigger, birds-eye-view perspective on the craft of world-changing. When we get involved in a cause, it's normal to look a couple of hundred years back in recent history, and see the industrial devastation and human rights abuses, then look at the world today and all that is wrong with it. In this narrow slice of time, we can often see only the discrete traumatic events: a forest felled, a seabird dead from eating its body weight in plastic, a polluted city skyline, or whatever outrage is littering social media feeds. But what if we zoom our perspective of time out a little—or a lot? What does our time here on Earth look like when viewed as part of a spectrum of a million, or even a billion, years? When we look at the origin of the universe, and *its own* evolution, a fascinating pattern of increasing beauty and complexity emerges.

The universe didn't start with all the planets, stars, and atoms it has now. It started with a field of energy. Out of the energy field came sub-atomic particles, and after a while, they started to stick together to form atoms. Inside the furnace of the universe's early stars, small atoms bonded together to make larger atoms. Atoms then crystallized into molecules, and molecules ultimately bonded into planets. Then came one of the biggest leaps of all: molecules started to self-replicate, and these self-replicating molecules formed DNA—the origin of life. Then from the chemical desire of DNA molecules to replicate themselves, came the first amoebas, fish, dinosaurs, chameleons and more recently, humans.

This increasing complexity continued as human and animals started to use tools. It didn't take long (relatively speaking) for primitive tools and crafts to evolve into machines like cars, aircraft, microchips, and wifi. The more technology we had, the more art people could make; technology enables the making of music, painting, dance, architecture, fashion, books, stories, and films. It's all part of the universe's invisible creative hand. This story is told beautifully by Kevin Kelly in his book *What Technology Wants.* Kelly explains the relationship between biological evolution and technological evolution, eloquently hypothesizing that our rapidly growing technical complexity is a natural extension of biological evolution.

No one knows why this energy that started the universe keeps evolving into ever more complex and advanced molecules, organisms, machines, social structures, and artwork. I choose to believe that it's an inherent, inbuilt creative force that runs through all of us right down to the energetic bonds in our DNA, and our purpose in life is to embrace it, to live it, to inhale it, and manifest what it wants of us.

We aren't just blobs of animal life, consuming food and electricity and *stuff,* with nothing more to contribute to the world than our environmental footprint. We are a part of something big—a majestic universe-scaled symphony of energy, atoms, and life, that has come together to create things, and it is evolving ever more quickly. The universe is not beckoning us to go back into the hut, or be stuck feeling ashamed and angry at the world's littered plastic: the universe is beckoning us to *evolve.*

Technology has enabled massive destruction. It's enabled us to cut down trees faster, make chemicals more poisonous, and burn ever bigger mountains of coal. But it's also enabled great improvements. The invention of toilets stopped children from commonly dying of cholera. The printing press brought books, literacy, and education to entire populations. The invention of catalytic converters slashed the heavy air pollution rates of the 1950s and 60s in developed countries. The world is filled with technological solutions that have made it an objectively better place.

I love how these words by astronaut Neil Armstrong capture the powerful and

The universe over

Once upon a time, the universe was a shapeless, formless mass of energy. Ever since then, it has been growing in complexity. Energy fields evolved into atoms. Atoms eventually formed into planets and stars. On Earth, molecules arranged themselves into the shape of DNA, giving rise to life. Then came the first amoebas, animals, and people, who can craft complex things of their own. You are a part of this mystery, its current incarnation. and you have it in your power to carry this vast, magnificent process, which has been going on for billions of years, forward. An entire universe of creative energy is acting through you.

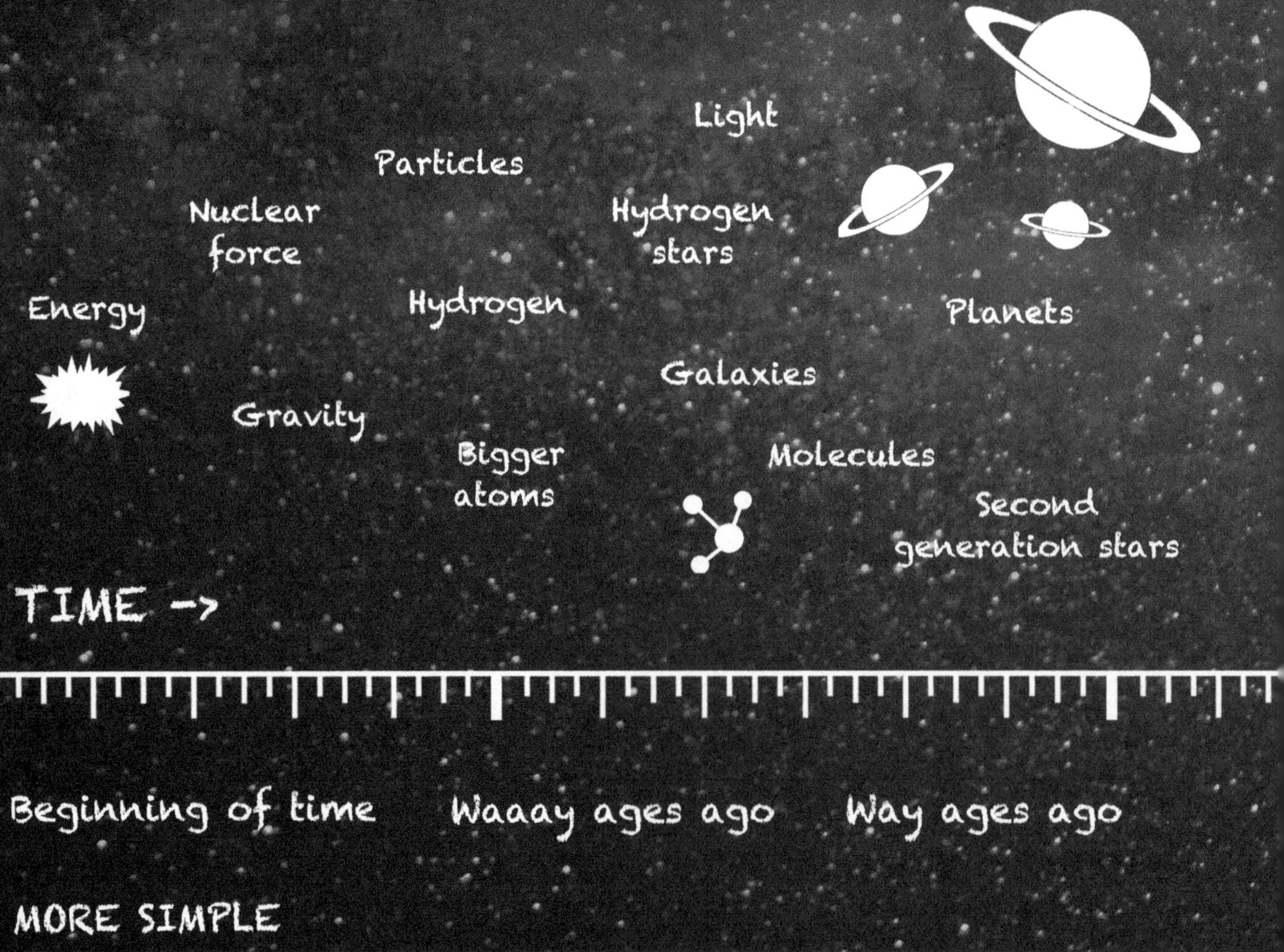

Light

Particles

Nuclear
force

Hydrogen
stars

Energy

Hydrogen

Planets

Galaxies

Gravity

Bigger
atoms

Molecules

Second
generation stars

TIME ->

Beginning of time   Waaay ages ago   Way ages ago

MORE SIMPLE

time

YOU ARE HERE

Electricity

Books

Your creative
contribution

THE FUTURE

Sunflowers

DNA

Houses

The internet

Furry
animals

Self replicating
chemicals

Synth-pop

Art

Lizards

Satellites

Amoebas

Microscopes

TIME ->

Ages ago   More recently   Now   The future

MORE COMPLEX

It is going to take epic
imagination, big inspiration,
and momentous creativity
to come up with the ideas,
innovations, and social
movements that will solve
the world's many crises.

innate drive humans have to explore, create, invent, learn, and problem-solve, *"I think we're going to the moon because it's in the nature of the human being to face challenges. It's by the nature of his deep inner soul . . . we're required to do these things just as salmon swim upstream."* It's common for people who have completed great creative works or made scientific breakthroughs to say that it wasn't really them who made it, or that they channeled some kind of external force. When we give ourselves over to the creative force and channel it, it takes us over and beautiful things can be born.

Some people are scared of technology, but there is no need to be hesitant about diving in. The world's progress moves forward at the speed of technical breakthroughs. Seven years ago, I sat around a breakfast table table in Silicon Valley with people who were building one of the world's first DIY satellites, and just five years later, a flock of these satellites now helps forest NGOs detect deforestation and illegal mining *as it's happening* and stop it on the ground. Satellite technology directly helps to save the forest. It's breakthroughs in battery and charging technology that are allowing electric vehicles to replace gasoline-powered cars. Every environmental and social problem has a technology issue that needs to be broken down and re-invented. Recognize technology not as an evil, or as something unattainable or overly difficult, but as a frontier in which you can invest your creative self to make a lasting, measurable impact.

Magic in the Confluence

Big leaps happen when people mix domains of knowledge that were previously separate. They come from mixing fields such as biology with hardware hacking, graphic design with civic engagement, architecture with mental health, or environmental science with theater.

Jesse Schell, the author of *The Art of Game Design*, talks about a delightful moment in his life when he was a young teenager learning to juggle at a juggling festival. He writes about how all the jugglers learn new tricks by basically just copying each other. There was one juggler he noticed who had a special style that no one could copy. Apparently, he was magnificent and he emanated an other-worldly quality of juggling style. He shared this with the young Jesse, *"You wanna know the secret? The secret is: don't look at other jugglers for inspiration, look everywhere else."*

The juggler showed him a move he learned from the New York Ballet, one move inspired by a flock of geese, and another by a paper punch machine. Several other jugglers were trying to copy him, but they couldn't. *"These guys can copy my moves, but they can't copy my inspiration."* Schell ends the story by saying, *"I wish I knew his name because his advice changed my approach to creativity forever."* Adding game design to the confluence of your profession and the craft of world-changing teaches us to remove the shackles that our siloed careers plonk us in.

Like a tree growing new branches, the world is full of emergent niches that are coming together in new confluences. If you haven't found your special branch, then reach outside your field and learn everything you can: study storytelling, psychology, graphic design, public speaking, machine learning—whatever. Scour the world for what it has to teach you. I found magic by mixing data science, behavioral psychology, and game design with environmental problems. I only discovered this trove of inspiration by walking far from my conventional training in environmental engineering and sampling widely until I got my own special recipe just right.

Knowledge & The Virtuous Cycle of Creativity

We often think that creativity is some God-given gift that doesn't really have a structure. We think it just happens—BAM—like a lightning bolt from the sky, or only grows from people who wear funny glasses and work in quirky designer office spaces. Here's the secret to unleashing your own creative potential—it's entirely dependent on learning. The more *knowledge* you have, the more *creative* you can be.

When you can learn how to program an Arduino micro-controller, you can make a light that flashes color to communicate something important. When you learn graphic design software, you can make signs, books, and stickers that get people to do more good things. When you understand the thermal properties of materials, you can redesign buildings to save energy. Everything you learn is an investment in your creative engine.

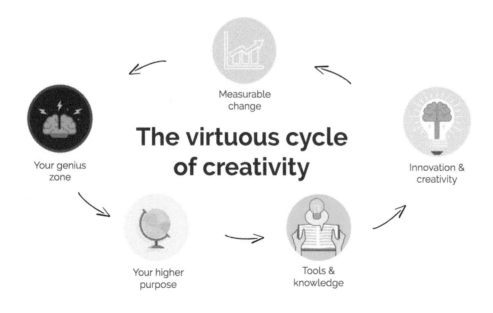

> # "These guys can copy my moves, but they can't copy my inspiration."
> — Juggling Man

Think of the sheets of music a pianist needs to learn in order to compose a new symphony or the nuances of light and shade that an illustrator needs to study in order to create art. A world-changer needs to study, too. All of the conversations you've ever had with interesting people, the data tables you've analyzed, and the reports you've scoured are stored in your mental hard drive. Your imagination scans that hard drive every time you are thinking through a problem. All this knowledge is translated into *creativity*.

Enlightenment is Now

Even though it's easy to think that everything on the planet is getting worse, it's not true. The world is actually getting better, much better. If you zoom out one thousand years, you can see the remarkable progress of human civilization. Every decade, things gets better on nearly everything you could want to measure, in just about every part of the world. The line is not linear, and sometimes things get worse before they get better, but overwhelmingly, the trend is upward. A lot of people find this hard to believe. Harvard professor Steven Pinker illustrates a detailed thesis on the evolution of humankind in his book *The Better Angels of Our Nature*, out of a frightfully violent history and into our recent awe-inspiring progress of relative peace, safety, and stability. A related book, *Factfullness* by Hans Rosling, shows how many of the things we fear—nuclear weapons, dictatorships, violent crime, infant mortality, and many more—are all becoming less common.

It's actually pretty hard to find something that is *not* getting better. Even when it comes to carbon emissions, the seemingly intractable environmental issue of our time, American emissions have been declining since the late 2000s.(5) We are not out of the woods yet, but many developed countries have recently crossed to the other side of peak carbon emissions. The upward spiral of humanity, which you are a part of, is making and always has been making extraordinary progress.

I believe we are going through an era of massive planetary enlightenment. It's not the first one or the last, but it is unique to our time on Earth right now. We are shedding many established ways of doing things. For example, exploratory

Some bad things decreasing

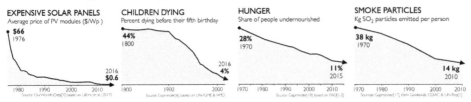

Some good things increasing

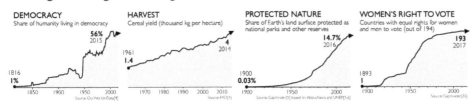

Some good things increasing and bad things decreasing: from Factfullness by Hans Rosling.

learning styles are evolving out of the old-guard of heavily structured school curriculum. The scientific community is validating the value of long-held spiritual practices like yoga, prayer, and meditation. Machines continue to automate many functions that living humans used to do: everything from mowing lawns, to selling books, to answering the phone.

Since history was first documented by the ancient Greeks, people have always yearned to answer the great questions of life, but modern progress has put us in a new position. We can no longer rely on the type of social structures that were common in our parents' era. Instead out search for meaning has become individualized. We are *all* yearning to find our special calling. Many people are now desperately pursuing the search for meaning beyond money or extrinsic prestige in their careers. We need to upgrade not just our practical technical skills to stay relevant in the new economy, but also to upgrade our *inner* self. All these things weave together: humanity's progress out of violence, ever-increasing automation by technology, new scientific discoveries—it all leads us further into our inner quest to make our greatest contribution to the world in a way that feels as unique as our own fingerprint. This is *our* modern enlightenment.

Your Life's Purpose: Unique Creativity + Measurable Impact

Your creative genius needs more than to just be recognized and activated. It needs to be put to work—and put to work in a way that isn't stuck in a desk drawer, DropBox folder, or in a garden for no one to see. Creativity needs to be put to work in the communities around us so it can have an impact that is *measurable*. It's is not meant to be trapped in a vacuum—creativity's destiny is to be shared.

I thought a beautiful metaphor to describe this interdependent relationship between creativity and measurable impact was the light prism that channels white light and turns it into a stream of rainbows (like the Pink Floyd album cover.) We need to cultivate our own creative energy, like the white light on the left-hand side of the prism, and channel it through a project or job that has the capacity to turn our efforts into change—our unique signature magnified and shared with the world.

Creative expression doesn't need to be fancy or born out of privilege. If your creative genius comes out though growing your own tomatoes, you can look for a prism to channel your tomato-growing gift. You might talk to your local school, and volunteer to help the students grow tomato plants, and with this application of your craft, you can measurably influence hundreds of families to eat better, use less plastic, and get in touch with nature through gardening.

Your Homework: One Hour Per Day in the Creative Zone

Your creative energy needs to be fed, and there is one nutrient it needs more than anything else: *time*. Just like a plant needs water, creativity needs a specific allotment of *time* every day so it can grow.

Ph.D. Psychologist Gay Hendricks explains in his book *The Big Leap* that working within one's genius zone is the key to happiness and enlightenment, and pretty much everything else good in life. He says everyone has a genius zone, absolutely everyone. The book resonated with me because I had always felt that I had a special creative genius zone that I was meant to share with the world. But the voice of my genius zone had so frequently been crowded out by all the junk advice you hear like *get more things done faster, answer all your emails, you're not smart enough to do that, save more money,* or *write down the calories you eat for each meal*. I was never really sure that getting behind my genius zone was the best move. It always seemed a little crazy, self-indulgent, and perhaps even irresponsible. Perhaps you have felt that way, too.

I made a commitment to myself two years before this book was published that I would invest exactly one hour every day into my creative genius zone of putting

Channel your creative energy through a project or technique that magnifies your gifts into real and measurable change.

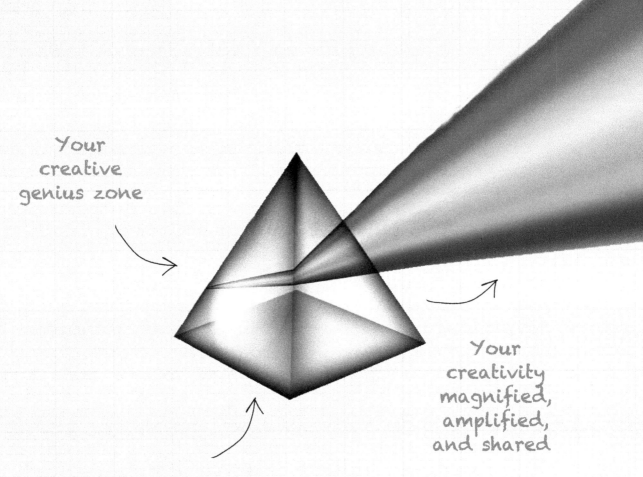

Your creative genius zone

Your creativity magnified, amplified, and shared

A project or strategy that enables you to make positive measurable change in the world

together the story in this book. What happened was incredible. I immediately tumbled into the slipstream of intensely focused inspiration. I created the talks, friendships, meetup groups, a podcast, and concept designs I had been wanting to for years. From a PowerPoint I had sketched out a few years earlier, I created this book. A commitment of only one hour suddenly turned into two years of work. I've had similar experiences with different projects that ebb and flow between frustration, boredom and great inspiration. But every time I re-ground myself and commit to spending one hour, or one whole day, digging into my creative genius zone, incredible things happen—and they happen quickly.

I want you to make a commitment to spend one hour per day doing something that digs right into the core of your creative genius zone. Do the thing you always wanted to do. The thing you have been afraid to do. Do the thing you never had the time to do. It's easy *not* to do it. There is every valid excuse anyone could ever invent to avoid it. Diving into your creative genius zone takes guts, and the time you devote to it usually needs to be fought for ruthlessly. *But it's worth it.* Your creative genius zone is where the magic happens. It's where the great works of art, beautiful songs, speeches, and scientific breakthroughs come from. If you truly want to save the world, which I think you do, your path to saving the Earth you love, and becoming the person you want to be, will come when you make the creative genius zone part of your daily modus operandi and focus doggedly on drawing it out of you so much that it becomes the core identity of who you are.

Think Beautifully

Don't waste your life paddling in the shallows of your calling. Move past your fears of letting your creative self out to play and push whatever it is you make to be a more brilliant version of what it was the day before. That's where the mind-blowing, world-changing moments that inspire generations come from—and yours will, too. The environmental movement has been so burdened a sense of guilt of stopping bad things happening, we have forgotten to cultivate our own joyful creative energy. Who knows what you can spark when you fearlessly unearth your own unique creative self-expression?

Gandhi said, *"Be the change you want to see in the world."* When we can all grow this kind of inspired fertility in ourselves, we can grow it in the world. It's time to give yourself permission to bloom. Let's flourish into our greatest potential and get to work making the vibrant world of our dreams come true.

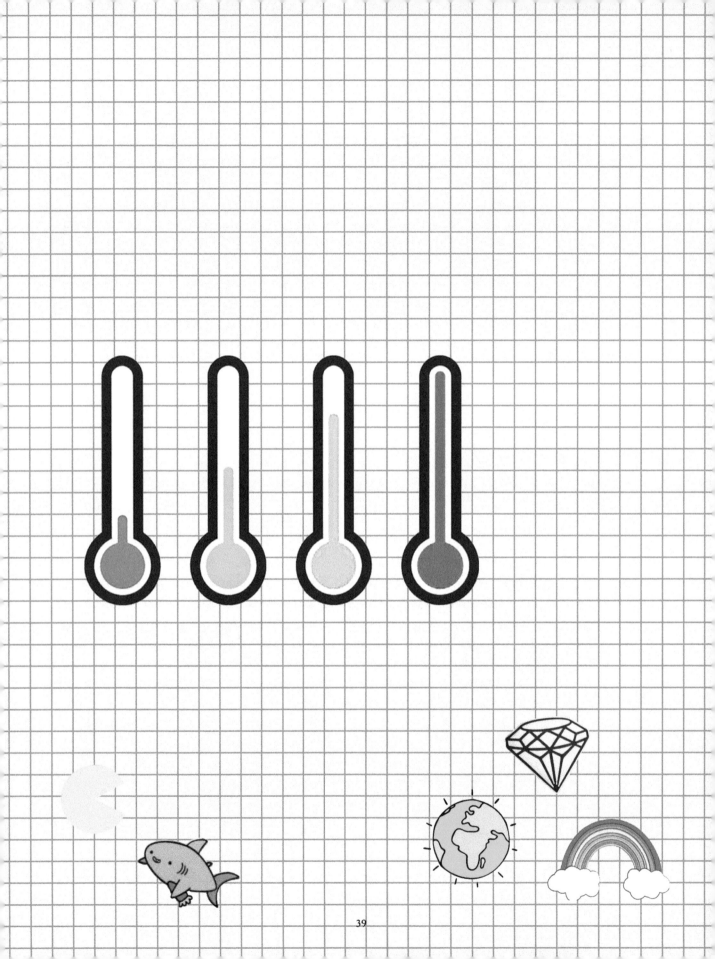

HOW I
GOT HERE

"The important thing is not to stop questioning. Curiosity has its own reason for existing." — Albert Einstein

It all started one day in 2013 when I decided to write some code. Zynga games built into Facebook were big at the time and I thought it would be fun to try and build a digital thermometer people could embed on their Facebook profiles that showed how much energy their homes were using in real time. I thought I could make saving energy fun, like a game.

Around this time, I learned what the word *agency* meant in game design. A player's agency refers to a player's *motivation*, or his or her own sense of ability to influence the game through his or her own actions. I thought that if people like me who were trying to encourage energy efficiency could pull the user's real time electricity data into the thermometer, we could create the *agency* we needed to motivate people to reduce their energy use. I got to thinking that maybe we could use the features that games use to make them fun: points, red dot notifications, leaderboard, and cute things like a digital strawberry award for high performers. I fantasized about the cute, weird, creative, and unconventional ways we could make environmental change as fun as a game, and I was excited to get to work on it.

I'd been learning computer programming for a couple of years and had fun mocking up my thermometer prototype in PHP, but then it came time to feed the user's real-time energy data into the app. It didn't take long to see that this data was unlikely to be easily available. A little more searching revealed that this was also the case for any other data feed about a person's environmental footprint—such as water, trash, or air pollution—that I might want to feed into a widget, app, or online game. No matter what kind of environmental data I looked for, it was often years old and trapped in a PDF document, and it wasn't available in any kind of granular detail. There was no available data for a single house, a street, or a school—only aggregate numbers for entire cities or states.

As a budding app developer, I could not get my computer to retrieve or query any data set I wanted with a digital request. This meant I couldn't show people pie charts, bar graphs, or leaderboards about their environmental impact. It suddenly seemed insanely obvious—how was anyone meant to reduce their environmental footprint without the data to see something as simple as how much trash they put out last month? It seemed impossible to design a "game for change" that has the capacity to tap into our motivational core (which games are meant to do) if anyone trying to influence people's behavior can't show their subjects measurable data about how well they are doing. It's a gaping black hole in our ability to create change.

Around that time I watched a TED talk by Alex Laskey from Opower where I learned how the behavioral science of comparing one person's energy use to another in the message *"Your neighbors use less energy than you"* was the *only* message, out of a few different messages tested, that *actually* got people to measurably use less energy. I watched Jane McGonigal's TED talk where she talked about using games for making the real world better, and the need for finding a way to utilize the latent energy we have for gaming and direct it into creating what she calls *"an epic win"* for humankind.

The confluence of these things: feeds of real-time environmental data—the behavioral psychology of comparing people to one another; and the theories of game design—had a lightning bolt effect on me. I saw the next leap for humankind was in gathering environmental data like never before, using it for the *agency* in human motivation, in the way games do, and optimizing what we know from behavioral psychology to get humans to do pro-social and pro-environmental things. I could see a new world unfolding of environmental data APIs, sensors, and game-driven apps that would help us topple the world's biggest problems. I went hunting for the academic framework from which to study how data affects people and discovered the work of professor Archon Fung from Harvard University. He used the terms "disclosure" and "transparency" to explain the phenomenon of how public data changes things and, most of the time, it changes them rapidly and for the better. It was fascinating. I wasn't sure of the exact steps to take, but I knew that I had to follow the trail of the data, and how data influenced human behavior to take action, and the trail would lead me somewhere special.

I knew at that moment that I was going to spend the rest of my life devoted to building feedback loops of environmental data, designing them in a way that was visually beautiful, and of course, using them to influence humans to do more good things. I thought of the name *Hello World Labs*, that captured the joy of learning a new computer language, starting a new chapter, and opening up a new world of opportunity. So it began. I started Hello World Labs from within the undergrowth of Silicon Valley's hacker and startup scene with no clear plan yet for a particular product or service, but a vision for specializing in the emergence of how data influences behavior, and an aspiration to utilize feedback loops of data and behavioral science to make change happen in the most dramatic way possible.

Overwhelm to Optimism

I have a vibrant vision now for the future of humanity and how we live on the Earth. But it wasn't always like this. I remember what it was like to feel frighteningly overwhelmed, shocked, and enraged as I discovered one tragic onslaught after another on our precious planet. What follows is the journey of experiences I've had as an environmental change-maker, and how my world-view was shaped over the years. I wanted to share these phases to illustrate a kind of upward spiral of an activist moving out of the darkness of the murky first days of initial environmental awareness, and iterating my understanding of how change happens over and over again. I think each of our trajectories as world-changers is upwards, towards ever greater optimism, skill, and creativity.

When I was a young teenager, on the evening news bloodied whale carcasses stuck with harpoons were being pulled up on to a whaling ship's conveyor belt. Norway, Iceland, and Japan continued to whale in waters close to my Australian homeland, and the footage of bloodied slaughtered whales continued to roll. In 1993 we watched images of nuclear explosions violently disrupt the aqua blue paradise at Mururoa Attol that came with the 1996 French nuclear testing. A total of 147 nuclear bombs had been detonated at Mururoa.(1) Posters showing balding and bedraggled battery hens were never far from sight. In the mid 1990s the "free range" hen concept hadn't yet caught on and 95 percent of all hens were battery hens.(2)

A cascade of international boycotts was unleashed against Nike as the corporation was exposed for paying its factory workers what were considered to be slave wages. Workers were paid less than 86c per day and child labor was used in free trade zones in Malaysia and Cambodia. The world was shocked by the vast financial chasm between how low Nike paid its workers in light of how expensive the shoes were.(3) Charity advertisements on the evening news were riddled with heart-breaking images of skeletal children suffering from the Ethiopian famine. It was like watching horror movies on TV, but they were real people and it was actually happening. Meanwhile, there was a massive conflict over oil in Nigeria. When I was 15, my mother bought me one of Anita Roddick's (the founder of The Body Shop) books. I read with horror about a deep pit in Nigeria where Shell's private army threw activists to die amongst the bodies and skeletons of activists before them.(4)

McDonald's took center stage as the hate-child of the 90s anti-corporate uprising. After two working-class English folk made a simple flyer exposing McDonald's impact on health, litter, and rainforest destruction, the corporation lashed back.(5) What became known as the McLibel saga, epitomized a corporation's merciless hunger to crush anyone, no matter how small, who tried to speak against it. "McDeath" t-shirts became a signature look of the counter-culture of the time.

While some kids go to music camp, my high school friend and I went to a World Vision Camp where we learned all about the civil war in Rwanda that resulted in the slaughter of 800,000 Rwandans.(6) One particularly grueling two-hour seminar on the medical care of land-mine victims told in detail from the presenter's own experience on the ground as a medic, left us, both fourteen years old at the time, huddled in our Nirvana T-shirts and Doc Martens, glassy-eyed and aghast, confronted, and never quite the same again. We also learned that the Amazon rainforest was being logged at the rate of six football fields a minute. In the early 90s it was at its peak rate of destruction and showed no signs of stopping. (7) And we can't forget the dolphins! As many as 250,000 dolphins were being caught in tuna fishing nets every year.(8)

These are just a few examples I vividly remember. I was shocked. I was disgusted. I was ashamed to be a part of a world that did these things. I was so deeply hurt and saddened beyond words that the world I lived in could be destroyed like this, and few people seemed to care. Learning about environmental destruction as a teen in the 90s was like being trapped in a bad dream where you are trying to scream and the sound just won't come out. The iconic 1980s world we had grown up to love, that was built from bubble gum, synth-pop, and cool sneakers had become cracked, and with it so were our spirits. Our trust and faith in the world we were being groomed to enter, had become fractured, as we looked into the dark machinations of what really made up the corporate machine.

Then Something Changed

Then something changed in the world, and something changed in me. It was around the year 2000. I started to see the very beginning of a new economy emerging. With bright-eyed enthusiasm, people were starting up businesses that

provided ethical and sustainable products and services across every market niche you could imagine: underwear, accountants, sunscreen, roof-tiles, envelopes—you name it. You could now get it organic, recycled, fair-trade, non-toxic, renewable-energy-powered, and eco-friendly. Out of the ashes of a movement that had cut its teeth on fighting corporate wrongdoing hatched a new age of environmental and social entrepreneurs who were springing into action like sprouts of greenery after a fire.

The movement possessed a child-like enthusiasm for the new kind of world we were creating. People knew that we couldn't bring down the old institutions that were already there. We had to build something new. The counter-culture was becoming a *counter-economy*.

It happened fast. In one short decade, the environmental and social justice movement that had once been considered weird, fringe, or even dangerous, was undergoing a metamorphosis. It was erupting into a new alternative industry that was quickly making headway to become more accessible, more mainstream, and more fashionable. Major NGOs like The Green Building Council, Fair Trade International, and the Forest Stewardship Council were launching environmental certification programs, with big corporations joining the party and signing on. Companies were hiring for the newly coined position of *Chief Sustainability Officer,* a senior role that had never existed before. A spicy fervor was emerging for the science and business of sustainability with corporate sustainability consulting quickly becoming a respected and well-paid profession.

The old brand of grungy leftist activism had quickly been sloughed off like a cicada disentangling itself from an old shell. What emerged was a fresh new type of green economy that was well on its way to becoming the often stylish, fun, and innovative sector we see around us today.

I immersed myself in this nascent movement from the vantage point of a corporate sustainability job I had landed in a large Australian property company. It was a fascinating time because corporate sustainability was an almost untouched landscape. I took the leap from skateboard to Italian leather heels, ready to take on the corporate world from the inside. It worked out. My sparks of environmental enthusiasm were a novelty taken on favorably by my pin-striped colleagues. I felt like Lara Croft on a mission to save the world, hunting for that one cog I could influence that made the machine turn. I was sure that in there somewhere, I could find the one cog that ruled them all.

It seemed pretty obvious to me at the time that we desperately needed to shift consumer spending away from the horrors of the toxic-emitting, rainforest-destroying, slave-labor made products that had triggered the 1990s anti-corporate uprisings. Despite the new green economy sprouting, the bad products were still (and in many cases still are today) the norm. Almost every product, material, and ingredient in the many thousands of shipping containers that move around the globe every minute had its roots in an industrial process that had devastated an ecosystem, displaced a community, or poisoned a river somewhere on Earth. I thought to myself, *"Couldn't we just save the rainforests by getting corporations to buy recycled paper instead?"* It seemed like a perfectly logical solution. I got enthused by the idea of saving the world by promoting eco-friendly products as if they were little shoots of greenery that needed to be watered. The more we watered the new green economy, the more it would grow and thrive. Then the old polluting economy would naturally disintegrate beneath it. It was a nice vision to have—and garden metaphors always feel so evocative, don't they?

After three years working as an environmental engineer in commercial property, I started to see that the green movement needed a pretty substantial make-over. It was still early in the movement's metamorphosis and we had a brand problem. We were still uncool. Really, really, uncool. For some reason I'll never completely understand, the art of *graphic design* was a latecomer to our community. The shoots were growing, but they were still pretty small. We still weren't getting anywhere near the downpour of watering cans that it would take to get us to grow anywhere big enough to out-compete the old polluting economy and grow the new world of our dreams.

I felt the creative energy brewing inside me to start a media company to change that. I wanted to blow the image of messy, smelly, falafel-eating hippies that had typified of what it meant to "be green" out of the water and replace it with an image of sustainability as the most fabulous, fashionable, and fascinating show on Earth (which it always was to me!). With a mass re-branding, we could inspire individuals and major corporations to buy the eco-friendly things that would unleash a waterfall of financial support all our little sprouts needed to grow, and we'd save the world . . . so I thought.

Cover designs of Green Pages Magazines: Environmental publishing company I founded and managed from 2006 to 2010.

I launched a publishing company called *The Green Pages* in 2004 and produced beautifully designed publications and online media that helped to do just that—to re-brand the image of sustainability. The publications were fun and stylish, and the company was successful, quickly growing to 20 full-time people and getting $1 million in venture capital funding. Everyone loved to leaf through the magazines and see a whole new cultural story on how bright and stylish the new environmental movement could become.

As much as a great magazine can set a cultural tone, there was another blind spot that took me a very long time to understand. I assumed that making beautiful content in the form of books, videos, events, magazines, and blog articles, was somehow *in itself* changing the world. It's what I call "The Biggest Mistake" you read about in the previous chapter. Educating people about environmental issues does very little, if anything at all, to get them to make a change.

The harder I tried to tell a compelling story for why "your dollar is your vote," the more the reality of being able to articulate it in a way that felt intellectually robust eluded me. The deeper I dug, the more I learned of *the opposite*—of the limitations to the power of consumer spending as a kind of advocacy. There were powerful sociological forces behind why the eco-friendly version of every product, material, or ingredient just couldn't crack three percent,

or often even 0.3 percent, market share. I had built my world-view on a hypothesis that, while a reasonable first attempt at understanding the problem, when held up to real intellectual scrutiny, was flawed.

Don't get me wrong here: eco-friendly products and materials *are critical* to building a new world. They are pushing boundaries in manufacturing that says to the world, *"Hey, you can make shoe soles from crumbled tires,"* or *"Yes you can make insulation from mushrooms instead of fiberglass."* They also push the boundaries in our acceptance of new products like silicone "moon cups," electric cars, or reusable coffee mugs—all of which have met a wall of cultural resistance for the simple fact that everything is weird before it is normal. But hoping that nearly every person in the whole world's economy will drop the cheapest and most convenient item in place of a more expensive and less convenient item wasn't enough.

However, in my failed attempt at explaining how you can save the world by buying eco-friendly things, I did discover the field of *environmental psychology*, which I had not heard of before. For the first time, the academic papers I was unearthing started to explain reasons the "Your dollar is your vote" approach *couldn't work* en masse, as well as many other details about what *does* make environmental change happen. For me, still hunting for that one cog that would change everything, discovering the field of environmental psychology was like putting on glasses and seeing clearly for the first time. This new field had many answers in it, and I was hooked.

One morning in 2013, with a warm black coffee in hand, I started to sketch out my goals for the upcoming year. At the time I had been building an online green news media platform called greenpag.es. I envisioned my goals and I wrote them out in a notebook: reach 100,000 members, raise venture capital funding, reach 20,000 page views per day, and so on. But something had fractured. These types of goals that had once excited me in the past, now sucked the life out of me when I looked at them. They made me feel spooked, even sick. I thought, *"This is not real change. These goals are stupid."* There is no relationship between how many members I sign up to my green news platform and how many trees are still left on the planet. There is no relationship between how many people read or share a post and how many cars burn through petroleum every day. I truly felt as though I would die if I were to spend another minute making a post just for the goal of getting "clicks" or "likes" or whatever, even if it was for the latest solar-powered gadget or cute polar bear story. I felt these words playing over and over in my head, *"If you're not changing the numbers, in a way you can see and prove, then you're not changing the world."* So came the point when I opened Sublime text editor and started building my thermometer.

Over the next couple of years I gathered more evidence, case studies, and design techniques that can be applied to data to affect human behavior, and put them into a PowerPoint I called, *"How to Save the World in 10 Steps."* The case studies I found told fascinating stories of how slight nuances in campaign design or wording can result in dramatic changes, or they can result in no change at all. What I learned along the way is detailed here in this book, and woven into the ten steps that will follow. These steps are the process I use for designing software and environmental change projects today, and they have had a transcendental effect on my creativity and my ability to create impact as a social change entrepreneur.

I'm excited to help people have the same lightning bolt moments I've had, especially young people who are just starting out in the movement. It shouldn't take you 20 years to work out all these techniques like it took me. Using these techniques doesn't (necessarily) cost more. It may even cost less, it just takes a certain way of thinking. The good news is that this way of thinking can be learned, this book is here to help.

I think the reason these techniques that are commonplace in other disciplines haven't fully permeated the environmental and social change communities is that it's easy for different fields to become siloed. I hope this book, podcast, and workshops in the *How to Save the World* theme will help bring together the fields of disclosure of data, with behavioral psychology, with user interface design, with game design, with hardware hacking, with community-based social marketing. These groups of people tend not to mix all that much, so I hope to create a vehicle, a conversation, an awareness, to bring these fields of expertise together. We find the seeds of innovation at the nexus of two things coming together that have not come together before.

There is a Japanese Zen word "shoshin" which translates to "beginner's mind" and means this, *"In the beginner's mind there are many possibilities, but in the expert's there are few."* While some things have clarified for me, and I'm excited to share what I have learned with you in this book, there is still so much to learn and to explore, and right now, I feel like I am at the beginning more than ever before. I recently heard motivational author Lisa Nichols teach her students to say the phrase *"Anything is possible"* over and over, many times a day. In a world where it can be easy to become overwhelmed, we must invest every day in keeping our mind and creative potential open to possibilities. No matter our age, or level of experience, each of us is at the beginning of our next big thing—and it's this adventure that we need to save the world. When you know good things are about to happen, being at the beginning is the most joyful place to be.

Turn the page and let's get started with the ten steps, beginning with the root of it all, and my all-time favorite, *measurement.*

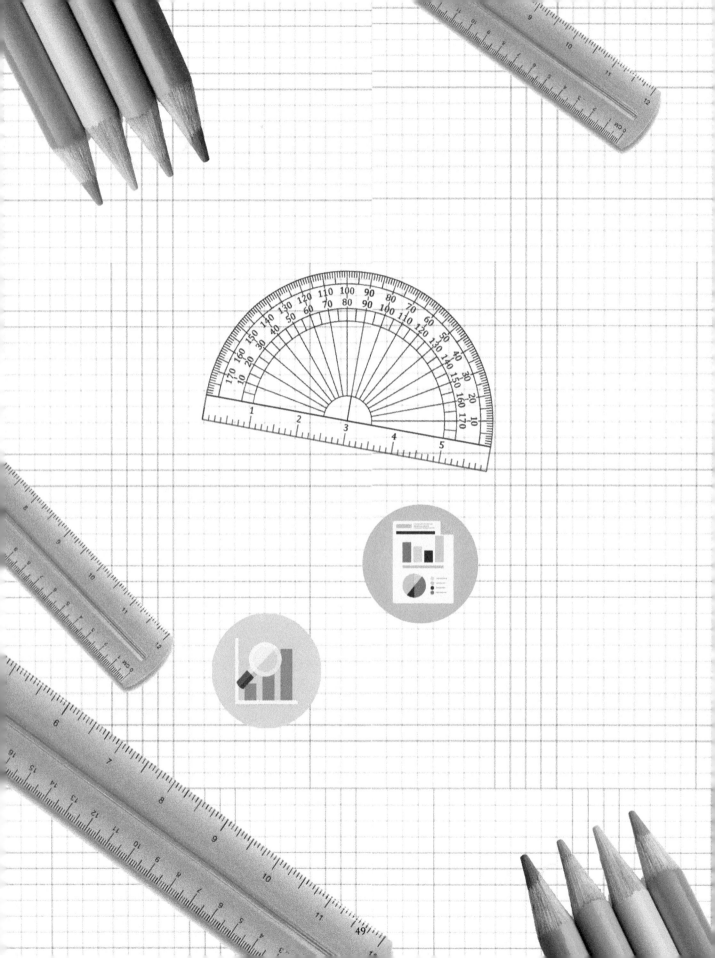

STEP #1

MEASURE IT

"If you can't measure it, then it probably doesn't exist."
— Common science quote

The first step in changing the world is to bring *the measurement* of what you want to change into the center of your universe. The data about your issue must be your first base—it's your starting line that all your plans, ideas, and your mission will stem from. People sometimes question if applying data metrics to the creative process of changing the world is a soulless activity that dampens the special energy it takes to dream up big exciting things. Quite the opposite is true. A strict commitment to measurability will fuel your creative idea-storming like never before. It unleashes new ways of thinking, introduces new design methods, and unlocks an exciting new world of behavior change and game design techniques that simply aren't available without it.

"You can achieve amazing progress if you set a clear goal and find a measure that will drive progress toward that goal in a feedback loop . . . This may seem pretty basic, but it is amazing to me how often it is not done and how hard it is to get right."

— Bill Gates, 2013 Annual Letter, Bill & Melinda Gates Foundation

Start practicing the art of drawing your creative energy from looking *deep into your numbers.* By numbers, I mean *real-world numbers* you can measure in terms of physical substance—not intangible and ephemeral business metrics such as clicks, users, views, subscribers, members, or signatories. A critical distinction to make when you are looking into your data is to be able to easily differentiate between *real-world metrics* and *business metrics.* Real-world metrics are measurable in *real-world matter* such as liters, kilograms, minutes, hospital visits, parts-per-million, square meters, or the number of trees—they are features of the *physical* world.

People frequently make the mistake of mixing these numbers up and thinking that what people do on the internet, on an app, or in a research lab is synonymous with *real-world change.* If you've built an app, written articles on a blog, or created videos on YouTube, don't forget that *what people do on the internet is not real world change*—not until it directly affects the *physical* world. One million clicks on an app or a video *are not* 1 million pounds of plastic taken out of the ocean. Even the sale of an eco-friendly product, such as a reusable water bottle, or an organic t-shirt, doesn't necessarily give the planet a net environmental gain. A ruthless devotion to pursuing a change in real-world metrics *over* business metrics is the thing that will actually change the world. At the end of each day, you need to be able to answer the question, *"How many kilograms (units) of x (matter) did we affect today?"* Here's why measurement matters:

Measurement helps you define your exact problem: You can't solve a problem that's not clearly defined. Defining a problem clearly, in numbers, will help you to discover a clear path to solve it.

You know if it's working: Continual measurement can be used to create a feedback loop so that you can continually and effectively evaluate your project's impact.

A united mission and vision: A mission that is centered around a quantitative goal will align your team, supporters, members, investors, clients, sponsors, and future recruits on a crystal-clear vision. It clearly communicates to everyone *what* you are trying to do, and *why* you are doing it. People can deeply believe in, and really get excited by, numerical goals.

The team's motivation: People need to see that their efforts to change the world are making a difference. Even small amounts of quantitative progress towards a goal provide a team with tremendous emotional validation to keep pushing forward. It's evidence that what they are doing *is working.*

Design for motivation and action: Measurement enables you to tap into people's deep motivational drivers by applying designs such as leaderboards, heat maps, star ratings, color-grades, and progress bars, each of which has been proven to motivate people to act. If you can get an immediate feedback loop of data, you can use your real-world data as if it were the points system a video game would use to give players a sense of *agency* over the game.

Super boost innovation: Measurement will open you up to new ideas and innovations you may never have thought of. Instead of getting hooked on one not-so-good idea, a measurement-driven process will help you to fluidly come up with ever-improving ideas for how you can influence your data. It will force you to develop really good ideas that bridge the Value-Action Gap.

Disclosing data changes things: Disclosing data, otherwise known as *targeted transparency* or *smart disclosure*, can create dramatic change. Simply showing people the numbers, at the right time and place, is a powerful psychological influencer.

Bypass silly ideas: A measurement-driven mindset will force you to distinguish between bad ideas that look fun on the outside, but aren't able to hold enough water to shift the numbers, from your really good ideas that will.

Reduce people problems: A measurement-driven culture should help to provide a more democratic work environment by taking attention away from the person with "the loudest voice" in meetings and focusing it on the ideas that shift the numbers.

In 2013, Bill Gates wrote an insightful letter on the importance of bringing measurement to the center of any social impact endeavor, *"You can achieve amazing progress if you set a clear goal and find a measure that will drive progress toward that goal. This may seem pretty basic, but it is amazing to me how often it is not done and how hard it is to get right."* It might seem obvious to measure what you want to change in the world like this, but the reason we need to make a big splash about it is because it's frequently forgotten, or flimsily tacked on as an afterthought. You'd be surprised how many social and environmental change startups and not-for-profit projects are launched, and even keep going for many years, without the team ever looking up the numbers in any detail on the cause they want to impact.

I've listed some types of common ideas to be wary of. These type of projects are prone to falling down the Value-Action Gap, whereby they successfully help educate people on causes but fail to get people to take actions that change the numbers. It doesn't mean projects like this need to be abandoned, but they do need to be redesigned for impact.

Events: Festivals, conferences, salons, drink-nights, and meetups can successfully get visitors, stall-holders, hugs between fellow world-changers, local press coverage, and good vibes. However, if you haven't designed your event with a very specific action you want attendees to take, and if you're not directly measuring the intended change, then it's unclear if an event actually has a positive impact on the environment. It's even most likely that a large environmental festival or conference has a *greater* environmental impact than if it did not exist at all, because of the carbon-intensive travel required by so many people to attend it.

Magazines, booklets, flyers, videos, podcasts, blogs, and websites: Creating content might spread captivating stories about serious issues, but don't forget, there is little relationship between your audience being *educated* on an issue, being *emotionally concerned* about it, and actually *doing* something about it. A high number of views on a video or blog post is not an indicator that those readers made any different actions in their lives.

Eco-labels and certifications: The nature of the eco-label model requires that eco-label organizations invest most of their effort marketing the eco-label itself as a brand and signing on new companies to license it. These two big tasks can substantially take away most (or even all) of the eco-label's time, energy, and resources. Perpetuating the label becomes the priority over pursuing tangible initiatives that shift the numbers on the cause.

Apps: The world doesn't always need an app to change it. A team might get so caught up in getting new users to sign up to their app that they don't see what needs to be done to make measurable progress on the cause. Some app concepts are an idea in search of a problem that doesn't exist.

Art projects: Artworks, exhibitions, public sculptures, murals, or poems may raise awareness or evoke an emotional connection with a cause, but if an art project is disconnected from a strategy for action, art projects by themselves are unlikely to change the numbers.

Games: An educational game might help people learn about an important issue, and do it in a way that is fun and engaging, but the game may still fail to drive any measurable behavior change in the real world.

Directories: A directory of ethical products or businesses may assist someone in their search for a product, and it might help connect some people, but a directory itself is unlikely to facilitate measurable change.

Online stores: Selling ethical or eco-friendly products can be a helpful resource, but eco-friendly product sales in and of themselves do not necessarily reduce a person's environmental footprint or an entire community's footprint.

Documentaries: A good documentary can create a powerful emotional connection to your cause, but making a documentary, or watching one, by itself, does not necessarily get people to do things.

Co-working spaces: Social-change themed co-working spaces are great for co-working, making friends, and building a community, but a co-working space in itself is unlikely to influence the numbers on a cause.

It's not that projects like these should be abandoned—not at all! They just can't stand alone as the *only* technique that will drive change related to your cause. If you create one of these kinds of projects on its own without designing it in *response* to the data, and without designing it as a vehicle to drive a specific *action* you want people to take, then your project will be like standing one domino up all by itself—it won't have the power to create a cascade of change. Your concept for change needs to be set up like a many dominos in a row. Your first domino needs to be the *measurement of real-world data*, and the last domino needs to be *a human being doing an action.*

Once you've comprehensively investigated the data, and how it is collected, *only then* can you weave together a fabulous strategy that is *built upon* your understanding of these numbers. Think of the data in your project as if it were the chassis of a car, the trunk of a tree, or the framework of a house. Once you have the core framework in place, you can start adding on features that build from your foundation. This is the process that will make you have *great ideas.*

I hope you fall in love with the art of measurement as much as I have. Even Paul Graham, the founder of famous Silicon Valley incubator, Y Combinator, wrote an entire essay on the importance of isolating a startup's most critical measurement and putting it in the spotlight. He said, *"Measurement will have an uncanny effect on changing what you are focusing on."* It's true, and the academic research reveals the power of it. With this sentiment, Graham urges startups to write that key number on the wall every day for everyone on the team to see.

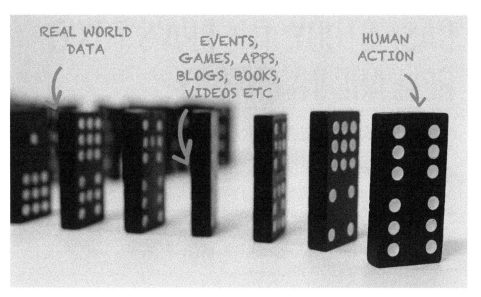

Dominos: an event, blog, film, game, or app, can't stand alone like a single domino and be effective. It needs to sit between your first domino—the measurement of data about your cause, and the final domino that falls—the action that humans will take.

The Power of Publicly Transparent Data

We can live in one of two worlds. In one world you can easily see information, like a nutritional label on a packaged food, a safety rating on a car, or a hazard label on a chemical. Imagine a different world where all this information was invisible. There wouldn't be any information disclosed that allowed you to rate or rank the products or companies around you. The world would be, in many ways, opaque.

It's easy to take for granted the publicly available information we have today. The disclosure of political campaign donations, the energy usage of appliances, the racial and gender profiles of people given mortgages, or the performance of your local high school, was once hidden—and it didn't get opened up for free. People needed to fight to make the government mandate that companies disclose information.

Why is the disclosure of information so important? Easy-to-understand data helps people make informed decisions and, more specifically, allows us to *compare*. Comparing one product to another, and also comparing *ourselves* to other people, is a core function in human decision-making, and a key driver of human motivation. There is a specific social influence technique that does this. It's called *targeted transparency* or *smart disclosure*. The theory of disclosure means taking data about issues that matter to people and making it publicly available. It's a different paradigm from which to approach change. A more familiar style of

CASE STUDY: THE EPA'S TOXIC RELEASE INVENTORY

One of the most striking examples of successful disclosure legislation is the EPA's Toxic Release Inventory, commonly known as the TRI. It came about when the EPA simply required businesses to disclose their toxic chemical usage. It spurred a staggering 45 percent reduction in toxic releases throughout the United States in the late 1990s.(1) What is so interesting about the TRI though, is that that the program was *never intended* to reduce chemical use.

The Annual Review of Economics, by the University of Chicago, explains the success of the TRI.

"The surprising fact is that without mandating any behavioral change, this law (Toxic Release Inventory) has had massive beneficial effects, spurring large reductions in toxic releases throughout the United States. This unanticipated consequence suggested that all by themselves, disclosure requirements might be able to produce significant emissions reductions."

"It was essentially a bookkeeping measure, intended to give the Environmental Protection Agency a sense of what was out there. The statute turned out to do a lot more. In fact, the requirement of disclosure, captured in the Toxic Release Inventory, may be the most unambiguous success story in all of environmental law."

"TRI's mandatory disclosure has done more than all other legislation put together in getting companies to voluntarily reduce emissions."

— Dow Chemical Environmental Manager
Millard Etling (Seabrook 1991)

"TRI is quite simply one of the most effective means we have in this country for protecting the health of our people, the health of our environment."

— Carol Browner, Head of the EPA, 1996

"The TRI is one of the most successful environmental laws in US history."

— Environmental groups (Hearne 1996)

REAL WORLD METRICS
YOUR GOD METRIC

All your efforts must lead directly to changing this number. Your God metric embodies how you will influence real matter in the physical world. Here are some examples:

- Carbon dioxide emissions
- Number of trees
- Liters of water
- Water pollution in parts per million
- Pounds of plastic
- Tons of coal
- Number of lives saved
- Time saved
- Temperature
- Wellbeing
- Body fat percentage
- Calories of food consumed
- Embodied carbon dioxide
- Biodiversity
- Crime rate
- Car accidents
- Gender ratio
- Quantity of medications taken
- Lifespan
- Kilograms of beef consumption
- Carbon emissions per 1,000 calories
- Gallons of gasoline
- Number of animals saved
- Air pollution in parts per million
- Pesticide use in parts per million
- Pounds of trash
- Numbers of fish caught
- Percentage of renewable energy

BUSINESS METRICS
SUPPORT YOUR GOD METRIC

Business metrics are not destinations in and of themselves. All of your business metrics must be carefully planned to directly influence your God metric. Here are some examples:

- New users
- Page impressions
- Attendees at an event
- Testimonials
- Clicks
- Likes
- Followers
- New customers
- Positive reviews
- Items sold
- Press coverage
- Votes
- Revenue
- Donations
- Signatures
- Members
- Email addresses
- Youtube views
- Subscribers
- Important people involved
- Laws changed
- Certifications issued
- Ordinances
- Events held
- Technology deployed
- Awards given out
- Books sold
- Documentary views
- Comments on blogs
- Market cap
- Market growth
- Funds under management
- Tickets sold

EXAMPLES

Business metrics examples

Don't make these metrics the core measure of your success. They do not define your real world change. These metrics are stepping stones that help you get to your destination.

Cycling: *Business metric*
+ Number of bikes sold

Meat reduction: *Business metric*
+ Youtube views on a vegan recipe video
+ Press coverage about a vegan restaurant
+ Number of people attending a vegan conference or festival

Women in technology: *Business metric*
+ Attendees at a conference
+ Members of a women in a technology meetup group
+ Press coverage on a gender bias issue
+ Downloads on a report about gender bias
+ Positive comments on a Linkedin article
+ Well-known CEOs making public statements in support of gender equality

God metrics examples

These metrics strike to the core of the change you are trying to make. Focusing on how to directly influence your God metric will reveal innovative and exciting concepts.

Cycling: *God metric*
➢ Ratio of miles cycled to car miles driven

Meat reduction: *God metric*
➢ Pounds of meat sold per day
➢ Pounds of carbon dioxide per calorie of meat consumed
➢ Number of animals slaughtered per day

Women in technology: *God metric*
➢ Ratio of women to men employed in technology roles
➢ Ratio of women to men selling technology companies
➢ Number of women on technology company boards
➢ Number of women graduating from computer science degrees

Business metrics are not by any means an unworthy focus. They make up the bulk of any change-maker's day-to-day activities, but the key concept is that they *support* the real world metric. Your entire concept will turn out quite differently (and will probably be much more interesting) when you perpetually brainstorm how to change your God metric instead of how to grow your business metrics.

advocacy involves bringing in new government standards that specify detailed rules that everyone has to follow, such as the thickness of roof insulation. If data is made public at the right time and place, it can have an almost magical effect of doing the heavy lifting of social change for us, without needing to usher in a more complicated or unpopular government intervention.(3,9)

There is a need for strict and specific environmental and health laws for some things, like getting lead out of paint and fuel. There's another range of issues that can be hard for the governments to get traction on, such as the carbon tax laws that keep failing to get passed all over the world. In the meantime, governments can do the easier job of forcing more data to be freely available, such as the energy used by individual commercial buildings.

Al Gore proclaimed, *"Putting information about local pollution into the hands of the public is the single most effective, commonsense tool available for protecting human health and the environment."* There's a good chance that if data about your cause is made publicly available, that people, cities, and companies will naturally improve their scores—and improve them quite dramatically. The invisible hand of disclosure is low-hanging fruit that has the potential to create a whole lot of change, and fast. It starts to get exciting when we investigate the case studies that show just how powerful a force for change public data can be:

➤ Toxic Release Inventory
Simply requiring businesses to disclose their toxic chemical usage to the EPA caused a 45 percent reduction in toxic releases throughout the United States in the late 1990s.(1)

➤ Car Fuel Efficiency Stickers
The fuel efficiency stickers on cars have influenced the average MPG to increase from 24 to 28 MPG since 2005.(2)

➤ Car Safety Ratings
Safety ratings on SUVs led to a 20 percent improvement in the safety performance of cars since the star ratings were introduced.(3)

➤ Restaurant Hygiene Grade Cards
Hygiene grade cards in Los Angeles restaurant windows that disclosed the restaurant's hygiene score in the form of an A, B or C grade caused health inspection scores to improve and hospitalizations for food-borne illnesses to decrease by 20 percent.(4)

Car fuel efficiency stickers: Left: European fuel efficiency label showing fuel efficiency as a number, a rank using letters A to G, and color. Right: American fuel efficiency sticker showing miles per gallon and money saved.

Restaurant grade cards: restaurants are given an A, B, or C grade for hygiene inspections and required to post their certificate in their window.

➤ Appliance Star Ratings

Australian dishwashers, compared to those of 10 years ago, use 25 percent less water. This change is attributed to the introduction of mandatory energy label stickers which disclose the energy consumption of the appliance to the prospective buyer at the time of purchase in the form of a star rating.(5)

➤ The Carbon Disclosure Project

The Carbon Disclosure Project led to more than 3,700 companies disclosing information about their carbon emissions. Since it started, Fortune 500 companies have reduced their carbon intensity by 2 percent per year.(6)

➤ Home Energy Monitoring Devices

A review of energy monitoring devices placed in households that disclosed the home's power consumption to homeowners found that these devices caused on average a seven percent reduction in home energy use.(7)

The Government's Role in Nudges and Public Data

There are big benefits to getting disclosure policies adopted by governments. It can be relatively easy to get the government to mandate that environmental and social data is made public. Most people like the idea of free, open, and transparent data, so it's a friendly cause. The University of Chicago's Annual Review of Economics explained, *"Mandatory disclosure of information is among the most ubiquitous and least controversial elements of public policy, often promoted as an attractive alternative to so-called 'hard' forms of regulation. Disclosure policies have proved highly attractive to legislators and regulators."*

The interesting thing about the disclosure approach is that both companies making the disclosure, such as car companies or appliance manufacturers, and the consuming public are free to either take action or ignore the information. Using disclosure as a feature of public policy opens up the topic of *libertarian paternalism* that is discussed in some detail in the book *Nudge*. It's the idea that it's ok for government and business to do things to influence people's behavior, while simultaneously allowing people the freedom to choose. This means that governments should keep overly prescriptive or draconian rules to a minimum, and instead provide a framework that *guides* people's behavior towards the most desirable action, while still protecting their freedom to make their own choices.

It's an important concept to understand because we do need to consider that lawmakers can fail to foresee unintended negative consequences caused by new laws. Laws that achieve the desired result without causing casualties are, in fact, difficult to design. The infamous War on Drugs has been a legislative failure. It resulted in the incarceration of hundreds of thousands of Americans, billions, or maybe even trillions of dollars spent, and failed to make life better for anyone. It's easy to think when looking at a problem *"We must ban this terrible thing!"* Humans are more difficult to influence than that, and there are other ways to get results. This is why disclosure of data is becoming a preferred policy option, because it leverages a hybrid of the best of both worlds. It uses light legislation to require that information is made public and doesn't require anyone to do a specific thing. Then it draws on the natural motivations in communities to improve their own numbers, in their own way.

A transparency model allows governments and social-influence groups to adopt a "lean startup" approach to change, meaning that everyone is involved—those disclosing the information, the local government, and consumers who can give feedback, can all practice a trial-and-error approach to change that allows iterative improvements on the system over time.

For example, it is quite difficult for governments to design a one-size-fits-all green building code. Each property's topology and each architectural design is

HOW TO DESIGN PUBLIC DATA SO IT WORKS

Data doesn't affect people all on its own. It has to be designed in a way that has influence, and designed with the human being who is seeing it in mind. Public data requires the following four features to be implemented in order for it to affect people.

1. Action

The data that is being disclosed needs to be designed to encourage a person to do *an action or behavior*. We'll explore more about how to do this with behavior mapping in Chapter Six.

2. Easy

The data being disclosed needs to be easy to understand. You can communicate data in a way that is immediately comprehensible using a symbol such as a star rating, an A-B-C grade, or a color.

3. Comparison

People make decisions by comparing things. Data needs to allow for the comparison of one thing, person, company, product, or property against another. You can design your data so that people can make these comparisons in an easy and intuitive way.

4. Time & place

Your data needs to be displayed or interjected at the right time and place when people are making the *one critical decision* or behavior that affects your cause. The vehicle fuel efficiency stickers are positioned on the car window *when you buy the car*—it's right there at the time and place when it matters. Likewise, a prompt to order a vegan meal is likely to be successful if shown when someone is ordering lunch or shopping for food at the market. If a message is displayed separately from when and where the desired action takes place, such as on social media, in a bookstore, or on a billboard, it could be too far removed from the pertinent moment to drive much change at all.

unique, making a top-down style of legislation that prescribes specific design details, such as the width of an eave, or the percentage of windows facing north, almost impossible to implement for every kind of building. A disclosure model allows the government to tread carefully around mandating these specific building features and instead focus on requiring public disclosure of the energy use of a property. The government might focus on requiring an energy rating of houses upon their sale, installing energy display screens in homes, or publishing a real-time feed of how much electricity a city's office buildings are using at any time. This public data motivates people to make changes while allowing them the latitude to improve their numbers using their own initiative.

There has been tremendous effort invested into both the legislation and the technology that has enabled us to see the data that explains the world around us. However, there is still much work to be done to make new data sets free and open to the public. Campaigners, technologists, and designers can all contribute to the momentum. Campaigners working in advocacy can lobby the government for more mandated disclosure of information and funding for sensors and databases. Engineers and programmers can focus their efforts on gathering more data from sensors and putting it into databases accessible by APIs. Designers, communicators, and social influencers can practice displaying the data in a way that drives people to act.

What About Eco-Labels?

Eco-labels are an attempt at publicly communicating data. They can either work well or not at all, depending on their fundamental design. These are the two main types of eco-labels:

Checklist labels: This type of eco-label involves clustering many environmental and social indicators together, kind of like a checklist. If a company, product, or building accrues enough ticks on the eco-label's checklist, they can lease the rights to display the trademarked eco-label for an annual fee. These kinds of labels show a single stamp of approval or verification. They don't disclose specific numbers and are usually voluntary.

Disclosure labels: This type of eco-label communicates an important number, such as fuel efficiency stickers, appliance energy efficiency stickers, or food nutritional labels. They are generally enforced by the government across an entire industry. They are not designed as a stamp of approval like the checklist labels, but instead show data (good or bad) in a standardized format that is easy to understand.

DESIGN FOR THREE LEVELS

Are you concerned that your audience might get overwhelmed by too much data? Often information is presented in a way that is hard for people to understand. You might be attracted to designing complex infographics or publishing tables of data that make sense to *you* as an expert, but not to anyone else. The trick is to communicate your data with three levels of complexity: easy, medium, and complex. The "easy" level is super simple. Then, once you have captured people's attention, you invite them to read a little deeper and move to the "medium" level. Enthusiasts can then move to the third "complex" layer that has the full scientific explanation, tables of data, and published reports. It's like a funnel.

Easy: Communicate your data in the simplest possible way using one graphic, such as a star rating, an A-B-C grade, or a simple color scheme, such as red, orange and green. Invite the reader to keep learning more and move to the next level.

Medium: Include more detailed numbers, the methodology you've used, and more background on the project. Invite the reader to keep learning more and move to the next level.

Complex: Create systems that has the most detailed explanation with your data tables and published reports.

DISCLOSURE ECO-LABEL DESIGN

Mock-up of a disclosure style eco-label for clothing that helps customers to compare t-shirts using color, star ratings, and disclosure of data. The label shows raw numbers of each t-shirt's environmental impact, designed in a way that is easy to understand and compare.

Star ratings to easily show performance

Disclosure of real numbers of performance

Color shading to easily show performance

Front of tag

Shows numbers in standardized units

Simple explanations of what each measurement means

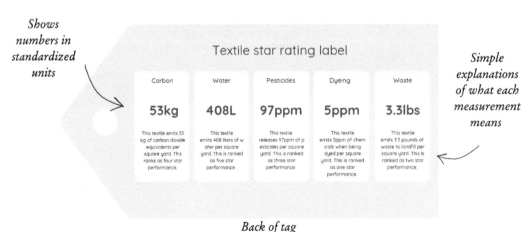

Back of tag

It's important to understand the differences between the two eco-label styles because, although the issue isn't entirely black and white, *checklist labels* are burdened with flaws inherent in their design that conflict their capacity to make a big change, while the *disclosure labels* offer a huge opportunity for growth and real-world impact.

The first generation of checklist eco-labels pioneered a wave of new environmental standards, but with them came a fundamentally systemic (and probably unforeseen) flaw—they require relentless marketing. The voluntary certification logo needs to create a brand in order to make it valuable enough for businesses to sign on and pay the annual licensing fee. If no one recognizes the label then the label has no value. This means the eco-label organization becomes, by the nature of the model, far more vested in the day-to-day job of promoting the label than fixing the actual environmental or social problem it is trying to address. Checklist eco-labels are designed as a badge of prestige or differentiation for the products they appear on, so by default, they only ever serve the top 5 to 10 percent of any market. This design makes them unlikely to improve the environmental performance of the other 90 to 95 percent of the market. Their value lies primarily in providing ethical branding for companies who are *already* environmental leaders.

Checklist eco-labels generally only have one level of performance: getting the logo, or not getting it. Some labels have three levels, like a gold, silver, or bronze standard, but the lack of transparent data robs everyone involved: the consumers, the licensee, and the certifier themselves, of the ability to use the super-power of *comparing* the licensees against each other by a single measurable data point. It also doesn't provide a feedback loop of data, such as the energy a building is using in kWh per day, that encourages continual improvement. Without being able to rank players from best to worst, to compare them to each other, or provide continual feedback on their performance, the checklist eco-label misses out on the most powerful drivers out there to make change happen.

The better model is a government-enforced disclosure label that is applied to *all* products, companies, or buildings in a market. Checklist eco-labels and disclosure labels can still work together to bring about the best of both worlds. The checklist eco-label can be applied as a kind of *award* to the top five percent of environmental performers of any market, and use it as a design framework to help push the market towards a best practice model. I predict that as data becomes more readily available, environmental audits will become more automated through technology, and more disclosure models come online, we'll see the phasing out of checklist-style labels.

I designed an example of a disclosure model label for apparel. It's a cardboard tag that would hang on clothing for sale. This label doesn't explicitly declare a t-shirt as "good" or "bad" by adding a certification logo. It simply discloses data about the environmental input of the t-shirt with a standardized design. The star rating and color bars indicate high or low performance. This type of design allows for quantitative comparison of one product against another, and it encourages the manufacturer to make continual improvements to better their score, no matter what their performance is. A disclosure label like this can have a powerful impact if enforced by government, and it can leave the upward cycle of change to be innovated by industry, NGOs, and consumers.

Why You Should Start Hardware Hacking to Get More Data

There is a chronic lack of data available on our environmental footprint. We don't know how much water we use on any given day, what the air pollution levels are on our specific street, or how much trash we make each month. Even entire cities and states can struggle to collect this data and put it on the internet. We can all get better at collecting data from all kinds of sensors, satellites, and surveys. We don't need to wait for a government department to do it for us. We can do it ourselves now, today, DIY hacker style. You might even discover an exciting new start-up on your hands when you dive in. Here's what kind of data we need and why:

Granular data: The EPA and government departments rarely collect data with granular detail such as data about individual people, businesses, or households. This lack of detail is robbing us of the ability to use several important behavioral drivers for change. First, if we can't find the data for our own home, college, or business, then we can't compete with our own score to make progress. We also can't understand our own score in the context of our neighbors or competitors. We can't generate maps that show where the heat sinks or pollution pockets are in a city without sensors collecting data that varies across every street.

Real-time data: We need data to be collected continuously in real-time. The immediacy of data is important so that we can see the effects of our changes on it in a feedback loop. Like a Fitbit or even a Twitter notification, data needs to update instantly, or close to it, in order to maintain our motivation. A study conducted on Opower by Harvard University showed that there was a marked spike in energy efficiency by residents after seeing the Opower chart in their electricity bill.(8) But their efforts dropped off within a few days, going back to normal for the rest of the month.

Machine-readable data: We need the data in a database that computers can search —not trapped in PDF documents or Excel spreadsheets. These formats cannot be

SENSORS & BUILDING STUFF

You can purchase all kinds of sensors and electronic parts that you can use to measure just about anything. With $100, some tutorials on Google and YouTube, a chunk of patience, and a dash of creativity, you can build your own system. Here are some examples of sensors you can purchase on the internet and hook up to an Arduino or Raspberri Pi micro-controller. You'll be able to gather data for your project with the detail you generally can't find from existing open government data. Sensors shown are from Sparkfun, Vex Robotics, and Symmetry Electronics.

Load sensors to measure weight

Particle sensors to measure air pollution

Movement sensors to measure wildlife

EMF sensors to measure kilowatts

Flow sensors to measure water use

Thermal cameras to measure surface temperature

Moisture sensors to measure water levels

Pressure sensors to measure steps

Temperature sensors to measure heat

Distance sensors to measure height

Satellite images you can turn into data arrays

Pollution sensors to measure water quality

NEW ENVIRONMENTAL DATA COMPANIES

The dropping price in hardware, the new movement in DIY electronics, and proliferation of app platforms have enabled the launch of a new wave of startups. They are gathering all kinds of environmental data at a level of granularity that has not been collected before. Can you use the data these companies are gathering? Can you build a startup that uses technology to gather your own data in a way that hasn't been done before?

Aclima: Air quality sensors attached to street cars that map air pollution data by specific address.

Essess: Thermal imaging of houses by street cars that help find heat leaks in winter months.

Global Fishing Watch: Interprets satellite data to track fishing vessels and prevent illegal fishing in protected marine zones.

Planet: Deploys flocks of small, low-cost satellites that capture high-resolution images of the whole Earth every day.

Conservify: Develops open source hardware and software solutions to help democratize conservation technology.

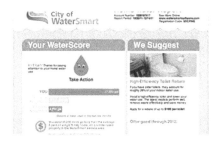

Watersmart: Reports how much water a home is using, and compares with neighbors, relying on water smart-meters that provide real-time water use data.

Energy displays: There are several kinds of energy usage displays and apps such as Chai Energy Bidgely, and Sense, that show homeowners or building managers how much energy is being used in a building.

Glow: A small colored lamp that communicates your home's electricity usage by glowing different colors.

Atmotube: Wearable air quality monitor necklace that interfaces with a smart phone app that shows local air quality data captured by your device and the other devices people are wearing.

read by web applications. Data needs to be stored in the form of an SQL or Mongo style of database that is callable from a web server. Imagine that someone wants to build an app that tracks the flow on energy-efficient vehicles, or map the pollution levels of lakes across the country, but the only data they can find is in a PDF. This is a huge stumbling block for the app developer. The more hardware hackers and scientists automate their data flow into databases, the more app developers will be able to develop projects that can help solve environmental problems.

Cheaper data: We need data collection to be cheaper. One constraint that is holding back the evolution of smart cities and widespread disclosure of data is cost. Sensors cost money and a lot of them might add up to a big bill. We can go a long way with DIY electronics though. When I looked for a wifi-enabled trash scale last year, I found a company that would custom make one for $2,500. I looked up some tutorials on YouTube and made it myself from the parts, with some help from a friend, for under $100. Things can be done inexpensively when you make it yourself—even technology.

Big things can start from small DIY projects. In the early days of Google, Sergey and Larry needed enough storage to download "the whole internet" (it wasn't as big back then) and run searches on it, so they started dismantling cheap IBM computers and sticking hundreds of hard drives together in their office at Stanford University. Every brilliant product started with a crude prototype.

"Measurement will have an uncanny effect on changing what you are focusing on."
— Paul Graham, Founder Y Combinator

Is Everything *Really* Measurable?

Don't fall into the trap of thinking you are working on something that is esoteric or unmeasurable. In every workshop I've given, someone puts a hand up and asks, *"But what about things you can't measure, like love or happiness?"* If you are interested in influencing love, happiness, or wellbeing, the good news is that they *can* all be measured. A quick Google search into the phrase *"qualitative research methods"* will reveal that you won't be the first one who has tried to do it.

There is a qualitative research framework for measuring even the most difficult-to-measure things. It generally involves either asking your test subjects questions about how they feel or observing their behavior. When it comes to your project, instead of working on *hunches* of what you think *might* improve happiness, love, or wellbeing, you can adopt a data-driven methodology, which will encourage you to read more academic literature, learn the qualitative research methods, and study the data that has already been collected. When you look at the numbers, you get better ideas than when you don't look at the numbers.

The Quest for Measurement + Action

Even when real-world data *is* central to a project, the teams of scientists and government agencies working on it may still have blind spots and not see potential features that can help their project make a much bigger impact. Whatever level of familiarity you have with the core data you are trying to influence, it's helpful to see *measurement* as the spine or trunk of your strategy, with the techniques that influence people to take action as the arms or branches that stem from that trunk. Each branch needs to influence a human being to *do a thing*. In upcoming chapters, we explore the kind of features, phrases, designs, and techniques you can add to existing environmental and social data sets that can ignite your project's ability to influence people. There's no point in gathering all this data and publishing reports if it doesn't ever influence a real human being to make a change, right? Your quest to change the world begins at the place where the data about your cause is today. In the next chapter, we'll define the future goal where your quest will take you.

EXAMPLE:
WHICH METRIC TO CHOOSE?

I've recently been working on a project about urban heat islands. The aim is to make a publicly available map of the heat island effect across a city in order to help encourage urban greening efforts, get property owners to install more white roofs, and motivate people to use less AC in summer. Heat islands are a complicated thermodynamic phenomenon that involves several nuanced metrics. Also, considering that we are trying to build a web application, there are lots of start-up web analytics we could also get obsessed by like clicks, subscribers, and new users.

A metric I could have used might have been: the number of people who looked at the website, the number who signed up to learn more, the amount of funding we could get, the signing of a sponsor, or important people on our advisory panel. There are a number of real-world data options to use. But which is the God metric? We could have chosen air temperature, surface temperature, reflectance, green cover, number of trees, energy consumption, ambulance visits, or cases of heat-related illness.

There were at least fifteen different metrics (both business, such as new subscribers and real-world metrics, such as roof temperature) that I could build our strategy around. I had to chose one, and it was peak electricity demand.

GOD METRIC
Summer peak electricity
kW/hr from 11am – 6pm
June, July, August, September

At the end of the day, our mission would be to say, *"We helped bring the peak load on the electricity grid down by 15 percent, meaning that five peak, inefficient plants can shut down, saving x tonnes of CO2."* That's the nut we have to crack. There are other metrics we'll need to achieve to get there, but like rivers to the sea, all metrics must lead toward the God metric. Otherwise we're just hoping for change, and not really changing anything. Our quantitative mission statement is *"Our mission is to reduce peak load on the electricity grid during summer by 50 percent around the world."* Our tagline is *"We make hot cities cool, lush, and green."*

Put your God metric on the wall

Make a poster with the number of your God metric and put it on the wall for everyone to see. Keep your consciousness wrapped around how to shift this number.

EXAMPLE: WOMEN IN TECHNOLOGY

Let's look at an example of how a mission-driven project might unfold differently with a "real world" metric versus a "business" metric as its core measure of success. Let's say you want to support women in technology. Your first thought is to hold a conference about women in technology, and so you get to work and organize a wonderful annual conference. You measure your success by how many women attend your conference each year. With this number as your prime measure of success, you are now getting really skilled at getting women to go to conferences. But no matter how many women attend your conference, and how great it is, these numbers may well have very little-to-no influence on the *actual numbers* of women succeeding in the technology industry. If you focus on a real world metric, such as the numbers of women successfully selling technology companies, you'll have a powerful medium to work with to develop better ideas.

Let's decide now that our real world metric is going to be the number (and ratio of women to men) of women selling technology companies every year. Instead of holding a conference where the only measure of its success is "bums on seats," we now have the significant challenge of trying to get more women to raise their ventures to a complete and financially lucrative exit, and that's a big deal.

You go back to the drawing board and think up a program called *Entrepreneur to Exit*. It's a mentoring and training program with five different levels, ranging from a beginner level to a final level where you help broker the exit. The aim is to bump each woman entrepreneur to the next level, with the final level being a company sale—your project's ultimate measure of success. Your new program might provide curated mentoring relationships, classes with well-known leaders, and introductions to the people in big companies who buy smaller companies. You might hold a monthly support group for women to brainstorm ideas about how to jump to the next level.

Level 1: Ideation to minimal viable product
Level 2: 0 to first 10 customers
Level 3: Your first $100k
Level 4: Your first million
Level 5: Ready to exit

The program is entirely designed to increase the number of women selling companies. That is the only number, at the end of the day, that really matters to your project. By focusing on this number, the organization will now get *really good* at helping women sell companies—an in-depth, complex, and valuable skill. You might develop close relationships with the buyers at large corporations—a powerful asset you can share with your community. You may even get into the business of brokering the sale of startups. At the end of each year, you'd be able to track how many women you helped guide to a complete sale. You are now making a huge and measurable contribution to gender equality in technology.

Think of how differently these two organizations would affect gender equality in technology:

Business metric focus: We got 372 bums on seats at a conference.

Real world metric: We helped seven women sell their companies for $5m+ and helped another 63 women graduate through levels in our program. We helped to increase the ratio of female-led acquisitions from 6 percent last year to 18 percent this year.

You may very well still hold an annual conference, but re-imagined with TED style talks where women tell a 15 minute story, recorded in HD and optimized for YouTube viewing, about how they sold their company. The speakers could hold workshops with the guests where they share advice to help your community of women reach their ultimate company sale.

With a real-world metric at the core of your strategy, the capacity of your imagination to invent better concepts explodes into something effective and fabulous. It paves the way for you to be in the position of not just talking about changing the world (like people do at conferences) but also doing something truly meaningful that actually changes the world.

STEP #1: MEASUREMENT EXERCISE

1. Determine your "God" metric
Your first step is to find the number that best defines what you want to change in the world. Your *God metric* must be a real-world number that is measured in quantitative units of physical matter, such as tons of carbon dioxide, or numbers of trees. Keep asking the question *why?* of your number until you have broken it down as much as possible.

2. Research your numbers deeply
There will be a direct relationship between how deeply you understand your data and how good you are at solving the problem. Research the organizations that collect and store the data. Pick up the phone and get to know the people who collect the data. Get to the know the technical mechanism they use to collect it. The data will become the soil that the rest of the behavior-change and game design techniques that we're going to learn depends on.

Consider the following questions:
➢ What numbers represent your cause's current status?
➢ Where are the numbers at today?
➢ What units do you measure it in?
➢ What organization collects the data?
➢ What hardware mechanisms are used to collect the data?
➢ Is is collected by sensors, by satellite images, or manually by humans?
➢ What software is currently used to store and present the data?
➢ How often is the data gathered and updated?
➢ What are the numbers per person for your city?
➢ What are the global numbers for the whole world?
➢ What is the national average impact of one person?
➢ What is the highest impact one single person can have?
➢ What is the lowest impact one single person can have?
➢ How does your city compare to other cities?
➢ Do you have measurements on how the issue is getter better or worse over time? What is the rate of change?

3. Work out how you will measure it
You might need to set up new ways of measuring the data you plan to influence.

➤ How will you collect your data? Have you researched types of sensors, satellite images, or cameras you can use?
➤ What type of granularity of data do you need? Can you get the data per person, per household, per street, per mine, etc.?
➤ How can you create a real-time data collection system? Is it possible?
➤ What software will you use to store and present your data on the internet?

4. Write it on the wall
Get a large piece of paper and write in big letters the numbers that describe where your issue is now. Put it on the wall.

Beware of doing this
➤ Beware of confusing your organization's quantitative mission with your organization's business goals. Don't let your quest for sales, donations, or new users muddle what you are here for. You need your organization's day-to-day operations to always support the larger mission that is defined by your God metric.

➤ Be careful of backtracking your strategy. If your organization has not been built around a measurable real-world number, you can make the mistake of trying to fit a number around it. Don't reverse engineer your existing project to fit around a metric. Even if it's just for the sake of making the most out of the exercises in this book, start fresh. Wipe your mental slate clean and think about your problem with fresh eyes, a fresh imagination.

➤ Don't cluster many data indicators together. If there are a few competing metrics, just choose one for now. Strip it back to the core measurement you want to influence, and then go through the steps in the book and build up a new concept. You're always going to get a lot more out of pushing in to your new (probably better) ideas that you will by trying to keep your current (maybe out-of-date) ideas valuable.

From here to there

450 kg per year   75 kg per year

STEP #2

THE GOAL

"To find the new world, we first needed a map." — Dalai Lama

Every destination needs a goal. If you are trying to lose weight, or save money, you probably have a clear quantitative goal to lose 20 pounds or to save $20,000. It makes sense that if you're trying to change the world, you'd have a clear number like this. You'd be surprised how many organizations and startups don't have a *quantitative* goal that defines *the destination* they are trying to reach. Between these two numbers: where the data is *now,* and the *goal* you want to get to in the future, lies the spine of your strategy that will change the world. All your ideas will branch from this spine.

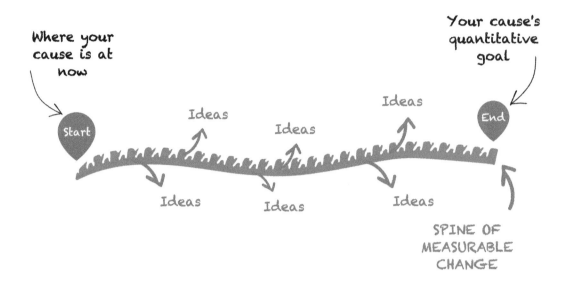

The spine of measurable change: your journey of change will happen between the quantitative place your cause is at now, and the quantitative goal you plan to reach. Your ideas and strategy will branch from the spine as you work towards your goal.

Now that you've investigated the data about your cause, the next step is to decide what number would best describe the problem you work on as "solved." What would this number be in a perfect world when the problem you're working no longer exists? This number you decide on is your *destination*. It is the x-marks-the-spot of where you are heading. It describes the dream future you are working towards. When the world arrives at this goal, this is the point at which you have won the game of change.

If carbon dioxide levels are currently 410 parts per million, your destination when climate change is "solved" might be 350 parts per million. If the childhood obesity rate today is 20 percent, you might define the problem as "solved" when childhood obesity gets under two percent. If urban forest cover in your city is currently 16 percent, you might define it as "solved" when urban forest cover reaches 40 percent. Don't worry too much at this stage about *how* you'll get there, that's what the rest of this book is about.

The next step is to write this goal into a quantitative mission statement. Many organizations write mission statements that sound so generic it's impossible to figure out what they do or to get emotionally inspired by their missions at all. Write your mission statement with a singular measurable goal in it, and you'll

Quantitative mission statement examples

Cycling:
"To have equal numbers of cars and bicycles on the road."

Meat reduction:
"To bring America's meat consumption down to 50lbs per person per year."

Women in technology:
"For men and women to sell equal numbers of companies each year."

Urban greening:
"To increase the green cover in every city to 50% of the urban surface area."

Conservation:
"For gorilla populations reach 5,000 in Central West Africa."

You want to become obsessed by your quantitative goal. Your strategy and your vision will come out of your plan to push the *real world today*, to become this *new world tomorrow*.

notice that the number itself is often inspiring enough. Your quantitative mission statement doesn't need to sound beautiful, it just needs to be accurate, and it needs to use *real-world numbers*. Some organizations struggle to define the deeper reason they exist and can have real trouble writing a clear mission statement. Adding one simple measurement to your quantitative mission statement will define *the core of your organization's reason for existing*. There is elegance in the simplicity of a well-thought-out number.

You want to become obsessed with your quantitative goal. Your strategy and your vision will come out of your plan to push the real world of *today*, towards this new world of *tomorrow*. Write your goal number in big letters on your wall. Put it on your business card, in your email signature, and on your refrigerator. Think about how this number would take shape when plotted out geospatially on a map. Everything you do in your project should lead to achieving this number.

You can even include your goal number in your organization's name. The 350.org campaign is a fabulous example of encouraging both data literacy and vision from within the organization's title. In fact, the only reason I can easily remember how many parts per million of CO_2 is in the atmosphere and that 350 is the number we need to reach, is because 350.org helped etch it into my memory. The other organization who does this is an Australian not-for-profit called simply *100% Renewable*. That quantitative goal is all there in the name.

You will draw your creativity and vision from this numerical goal. Einstein once said, *"Imagination is everything. It is the preview of life's coming attractions."* Your goal number is the centerpiece from which you can dream and imagine a new world, and by studying it, you will start to discover the ideas that can make this number happen. Clarifying your goal number will get you ready for the visualization process that we'll jump into on the next page.

STEP #2: THE GOAL EXERCISE

1. Choose a number: Choose a quantitative goal that defines your cause's destination. Make sure that your goal is measurable in units that you've thoroughly considered. Make your goal realistic, while still being ambitious and inspiring.

2. Write your quantitative mission statement: Write one quantitative mission statement like this: "Our mission is to reduce/increase

_____ (the issue) from_____(units) to_____ (units)

for_____(location/organization)."

*Example: Our mission is to reduce **storm water pollutants** (the issue) from **534 ppm** (units) to **75 ppm** (units) for **The City of Chicago** (location/organization).*

3. Explore quantitative sub-goals: It's likely that your master quantitative goal will have a few related sub-goals that will also need to happen. Branch off the master and make others for different divisions of your organization. You can have more than one, but each quantitative mission will have a different strategy.

4. Put it on the wall: Make a poster of your goal number and put it on the wall for you and everyone else to see.

5. Make it visible: Wrap your goal number into your organization's branding and culture. Add it to your "About us" page. Put it in images on social media. Put it on your website's homepage. You might even want to incorporate it into your project's name.

Beware of doing this
➢ Beware of coming up with goals that don't have defined quantitative units, such as building a movement, raising awareness, educating people, or spreading an ideology. You need to be able to measure what you are trying to change in order to change it.
➢ Beware of coming up with a goal that clusters many issues together. Spreading your energy between several data points means you are less likely to achieve change on a single one.

The Five Farming Bridges by Vincent Callebaut Architectures.
Winning Project of the Rifat Chadirji Prize - Competition, Rebuilding Iraq's Liberated Areas: Mosul's Housing.

STEP #3

VISUALIZE YOUR WORLD

"If you want to build a ship, do not drum up the men to gather wood, divide the work and give orders. Instead, teach them to yearn for the vast and endless sea."
— Antoine de Saint-Exupéry, French aristocrat, writer, poet, and aviator

It's all too common for people who are trying to change the world to get bogged down on focusing on the *problem*. It's easy to think about the world in terms of what we want to stop, such as, *"Everyone needs to stop littering plastic,"* or *"Corporations really need to stop that dreadful mountaintop coal mining."* It makes sense, considering the whole environmental and social-change movement was more or less born out of reactionary measures to terrible things, such as sudden news that your local forest is going to be felled next week. A problem-focused way of thinking, however, can be detrimental. There's a common mistake people make when choosing their words that is reflective of this problem-oriented mindset. Messages that tell people *how bad* everything is, such as *"72 percent of people waste water,"* or *"Twelve thousand plastic bottles are thrown out every day"* don't motivate people to change. They actually tell people it *is normal.* Because humans tend to imitate those around them, these kinds of statements can actually *encourage* the very behavior you are trying to stop. A sign at Arizona's Petrified Forest intended to stop people stealing the ancient rocks read, *"Your heritage is being vandalized every day by thieves."* This sign caused people to steal *double* the amount of rocks compared to a message that simply said, *"Please don't remove the petrified wood from the park."*(1) The first sign unintentionally told people, *"Everyone else is doing it, so you should do it too."*

I made some mock-up images that illustrate how silly it would look if major brands in their advertising, were to use negative images of what *not* to do. The art of advertising sells us the *aspiration* of the person we'd like to become, and it sells us an *association* to something we want to feel. Advertising campaigns rarely lambaste us with images of what we *don't* want to become, because advertising agencies know this approach doesn't work.

Being problem-focused keeps us trapped in an outdated way of thinking. Albert Einstein once said, *"We can't solve problems with the same thinking we used to create them."* Looking out for bad-things-to-stop keeps us in a mental loop of perpetually reacting to, or even being a victim of, the world around us. We still need to stop bad things happening in the world *today*, but we also need to design the *destination* that we are trying to get to *tomorrow*—and that distinction requires an entirely different mind-space.

This is the foundation of why changing the world is an inherently creative process. Think of how an architect designs a spectacular new building, or a screenwriter illustrates a story in another universe, or a dressmaker designs an

The creative mind: creative people are able to mentally visualize in great detail what they aspire to create, then they reverse engineer the mental model to bring their vision to life.

Be careful not to use negative images of what you don't want people to do. These mock-ups of popular advertisement show what it would look like if major brands used negative images to show people what *not* to become.

outrageously novel gown. The creator first *imagines* the thing he or she want to create, then draws it on paper (or computer), then reverse engineers it and figures out all the steps between *here* and *there* that need to happen to bring it into physical form. This is the core creative process: imagine; reverse engineer; create. It's a skill that creative people possess—they can imagine ideas in their mind as detailed, complex, and unique three-dimensional mental models *before* they bring them into existence in real life.(2) World-changers need to exercise this mental muscle by casting our imagination into the future and describing in detail a vision for the beautiful world we want to create.

A few years ago, I read that athletes commonly undertake an exercise in which they visualize winning a game or a race. This kind of mental rehearsal has a

Artistic rendition of a future city layered in vegetation and urban farming, by Terreform New York.

remarkably powerful effect on the body. An athlete sitting still in meditation, while mentally taking herself through her sport, activates the muscles, brain, and heart rate, having a similar effect on the body as if she were physically doing the activity. A Russian study found that basketball players who experienced *only* physical training performed worse than players who spent 75 percent of their time mentally visualizing themselves successfully getting the ball in the hoop and only 25 percent of their time actually doing the sport.(3)

When I learned about the phenomenal effect of mental visualization, I wondered why we never did this in the environmental movement. Savings forests isn't quite a game of basketball, however, I couldn't help but mull over what kind of equivalent muscle we'd build if we did the same thing when it came to changing the world. Maybe if I spent 30 minutes a day imagining us successfully reaching a 100 percent renewable powered electricity grid, I'd get better at *something*, just like those athletes. What would the world look like if every social change activist, environmental advocate, teacher, and visionary had her dream for a better world come true? What is our "gold medal moment" going to look like?

I started imagining it. It's funny, I was already in my 30s and despite being devoted to environmental sustainability, I'd never consciously pulled back the curtain and stepped into this mental realm. I started meditating on questions like this, "*What if landfills suddenly vanished? What kind of government system would*

Mock newspapers: *"News of the future"* by Jeff Skoll and *The Good News New York Times* by the Yes Men, each showing imaginary positive news they would like to see come true.

protect all of the world's forests and endangered animals? What would cities feel like if buildings were designed to mimic a living ecosystem? How could the entire Earth run on 100 percent clean energy? How would a school manage to grow all its own food on campus for kids to eat? What would an entirely car-free city look like? How could cities be designed for small children and families to live together in modern urban villages? What would cities look like draped in urban orchards and hanging gardens? What would a day in the life of an ordinary person look like when disposable plastic doesn't exist?" I ruminated on these questions, and then something magical happened.

My imagination lit up with new ideas of what could be possible. I had so many ideas, I could hardly write them down fast enough. It was like a vibrant forest of concepts had suddenly sprung up in my mind. I was no longer thinking the heavy and frustrated thoughts I was familiar with, about how to put out fires and stop nasty problems in the world I knew. Instead, I was mentally building an incredible new world: a world where I wanted to live, a world that I would be profoundly proud to be a part of.

I was filled with a feeling of lightness and joy, and an enthusiasm for the future that *could be*. Something in my own universe shifted once I could see a path to an ever-improving world. I had an exciting part to play in bringing this world to life, and in some way, this changed me forever.

The first time I saw something like this was at the Skoll World Forum social-entrepreneur summit. The founder, Jeff Skoll, mocked up the kind of headlines he would *like to see* in the world as if they were happening today. He called it *"Imagine the News of the Future."* The three-day forum culminated on a lofty crest of future-aspiration when he unveiled his striking headlines that declared *"Last Nuclear Weapons Destroyed," "U.S. Imports Last Barrel of Oil,"* and *"10 Years of Peace in the Middle East."* I don't know exactly why, but these images of a profoundly better future touch us in a uniquely sensitive way. Maybe it's because hope is stronger than fear.

A similar project was done by the comic protest duo, *The Yes Men,* when they created a real hard copy "good news" imitation of *The New York Times* newspaper. The mock paper was adorned with bombastically positive headlines that The Yes Men would *like to see* and distributed one morning throughout Manhattan.

There's a good reason that people need a positive vision of the future. Our brains are wired to have what is called *optimism bias*. It means that each of us believes that we are *less* at risk of experiencing a negative event compared to other people. For example, imagine you read in a medical brochure that you have a 50 percent chance of getting cancer. You would most likely think, *"That's ok because I'm obviously in the half that isn't going to get cancer."*(4) Now imagine you are told that the housing market is going up. You'll most likely think, *"That's great! I'll be able to sell my house for the highest price!"* Basically, we all think we have a good shot at becoming millionaires, but we'll never suffer a dreaded car accident. We can leverage the optimism bias. When we tell an optimistic story about a future world, quite simply, everyone will be more likely to believe it is going to happen to them and want to learn more about it and engage more deeply with anything related to this future scenario.

Inspirational tales of a future world are important because the anticipation of a future positive event makes us happy. People feel most happy on Fridays because they experience a sense of positive anticipation for the weekend. People are not as happy on Sundays, because they experience negative anticipation of the dreaded soon-to-be Monday.(4) Imagine we extrapolated this finding, and instead of looking at the weekend, we look forward a few decades. It makes sense that the positive anticipation of a wonderful world unfolding might also bring this kind of anticipation-laden happiness that we experience every Friday, but over a lifetime.

The anticipation of a future event *is* the very fabric of optimism—and optimists get a better deal. Optimists are more creative. Optimists are more successful. Optimists are healthier. Optimists are more productive. Optimism feeds a person's personal agency to affect change and work hard to achieve goals. It makes sense that if you believe that your dream world will one day come true, that you'd be more motivated to chip in your time, money, heart and soul for the winning team.

> "You never change things by fighting the existing reality. To change something, build a new model that makes the existing model obsolete."
>
> —Bucky Fuller, Futurist and Inventor

People who are prone to pessimistic thinking are more likely to give up on challenges sooner.(5)

Let's look closer at the need for happiness. If you're trying to save polar bears, does it really matter if your world-changing ventures help people feel happy or not, as long as the polar bears get saved in the end? Happiness matters for more reasons than because it feels nice. To come up with creative solutions, we need to be in a reasonably happy state. A Harvard University study asked 280 people working in various industries to record their daily emotions and discovered that people experiencing joy and love were *more creative* than people experiencing anger, fear, and anxiety.(6) Creativity researcher, Dr. Shelley Carson, describes it like this, *"Increases in positive mood broaden attention and allow us to see more possible solutions to solve creative problems."* Creativity is the act of doing, making or thinking something that has not been done, made, or thought before, and that's why creativity is the backbone skill in changing the world.

It's hard for people to think creatively when they are burdened by feelings of stress and fear. Here's why messages of fear and doom such as a picture of a burning Earth, stories of climate armageddon, and videos of tortured animals can be a terrible strategy to save the world. You might need to use them *occasionally*, but be careful with the dose. When the body releases stress chemicals, the brain shuts down the hippocampus region and you lose about thirty percent of your cerebral brain function—that includes the creative thinking faculties.(7,8) When we calm down, and that part of our brain reactivates, creativity and innovative thinking increase substantially. Psychologist Adam Anderson described it as, *"With a positive mood, you actually get more access to things you would normally ignore. Instead of looking through a porthole, you have a landscape or panoramic view of the world."* To simplify: fear and doom shut down your brain's capacity for creative thinking. Vision and optimism super-boost it.

Don't underestimate the power of a rich vision to inspire the people around you. This vision will be at the heart of your brand. It will be embedded in your copywriting and make up your tagline. This is the vision you or your CEO describes when giving a talk on stage or an interview on the radio. It's the hook

> "Optimists exert more continuous effort and tend not to give up . . . Pessimists, on the other hand, are far more likely to anticipate disaster – and, as a result, are more likely to give up."
> — Ilona Boniwell, Positive Psychologist

that makes people care, and it's this vision that will not only keep everyone around you motivated, but also become an adventure. This is the psychology behind Dr. Martin Luther King Jr.'s famous *"I have a dream"* speech. We all need our own version of the phrase, *"I have a dream that . . . "* If you are optimistic and believe your vision will come true, other people will believe it, too.

Now it's your turn. Your next task is to visualize what the world will look like when your quantitative goal from Chapter Two is reached. Get a giant piece of paper and start drawing your future world. You can also mind map it. Start by drawing a circle in the middle of the paper and write your data goal inside the circle. Then keep adding branches to the circle of your vision in words or drawings of what the world will look like when this number is a reality.

This is where it gets fun. Close your eyes and imagine this world. How does it work? What technology does it use? What does a day in the life of a regular person look like? What products do people use? How does the government operate? How is this world visually beautiful? What emotions do people feel? What does it smell like? Look at your visualization and work out the specific technical requirements needed to get there. This exercise can light the path for technology breakthroughs. Who knows what million-dollar startup is nestled in the sketches of your visualization.

Imagining this destination is a powerful exercise. It beckons you to dig into your creative genius zone and invent something wonderful. If there is a parallel with the visualization done by athletes, it might also catalyze your consciousness into doing what it takes to make this dream come true. Dare to dream big and let your imagination unfurl. Draw pictures of what these ideas look like. Write poetry or a short story. Have a creative workshop or art day with your team.

Take your time with it. This kind of work requires that your mind steps off the hurried, stressed-out, lots-of-things-to-do mental treadmill and invokes a slower, thoughtful kind of modulation. There's a system in the brain called the default mode network. Ph.D. psychologist Scott-Barry Kaufman, who studies creativity, is trying to re-brand it as *the imagination network* because it helps us come up with new ideas. It gets activated when the rest of the brain chills out by day-dreaming, relaxing, and letting the mind's attention wander. It gets turned *off* when we are

The creative circle

Visualizing your beautiful future world as an interdependent cycle of optimism and happiness that feeds the creative productivity you need to build a movement.

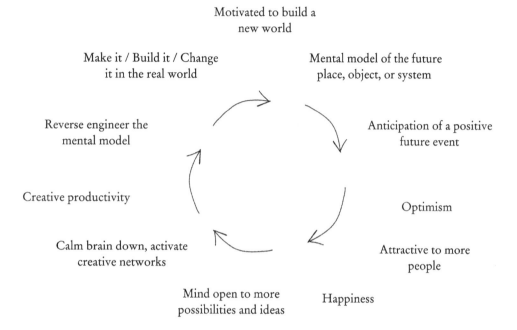

doing stressful or cognitively demanding tasks that require active focus.(9) Even the practice of mindfulness turns off the default mode network.(10) MRI scans show that creative people have a more easily activated default mode network.(11) Activating the imagination requires a gentle and slower kind of thinking, and that's why you need to devote a generous chunk of un-hurried time and space to it.

Stressing out about an imagined future apocalypse uses what's called the *neurotic imagination*—that's the bad kind of imagination that narrows the mind in on a single projected terrible event—an event that might not even happen. The opposite, and better, approach is to use the *creative* or *positive constructive imagination*—a term coined by research psychologist Jerome Singer in the 1960s. You could call the ecological version of it *the environmental design imagination*. It's the healthy kind of imagination that thinks up new ideas and solves problems, and it needs to do some pretty crazy cerebral feats. It needs to make intricate mental models of the future—like imagining what it would take to cover a whole city in vegetation. It needs to unravel big, complex problems, like how carbon emissions affect the economy. It needs to produce an abundance of new ideas—everything from bamboo water bottles to electric cargo bikes to new taxation

Central Executive Network   Default Mode Network

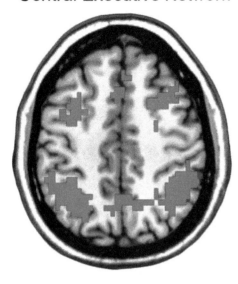 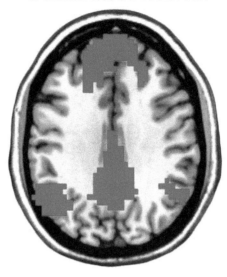

Networks of thought: cognitively demanding tasks use a different brain network than the network in the brain that helps to come up with new ideas and creative solutions.

systems—and then it needs to figure out how to reverse engineer all these ideas into reality.

You need to switch back and forth between *imagination* (from the default mode network) and *engineering* (that happens in the prefrontal cortex). This dance between *imagining* and *making* is the guts of the creative process of bringing an idea and a vision of a future world to life. To do this, your brain needs to relax, to feel happy, to be optimistic, and to have a dream. It's in that space where great discoveries, inventions, and works of art are born. It's where you'll find the kind of creativity it takes to save the world.

It's all an interconnected loop of creativity. The anticipation of positive future events makes us happy. Optimists are happier. Happy people do better at creative tasks. People are happier when they are creative. Happiness and optimism allow the mind to be at peace, a state in which it can imagine. Starting with a vision of a better world and making it come true in the real world is an inherently creative process. That's the upward spiral. This is *the creative process of saving the world* in action.

There's a Buddhist teaching that says *"What you think, you become. What you feel, you attract. What you imagine, you create."* Let's move out of an obsession with the world we *don't* want and start a revolution dreaming up the world we *do* want. You will shake many ideas from your visualization like fruit dropping from a tree. Now let's move into the next chapter where you will harvest your ideas.

STEP #3: VISUALIZATION EXERCISE

1. Paper and your goal: Get a large piece of paper and colored markers and draw a circle in the middle and write your data goal from Chapter Two inside the circle.

2. Mind map: Start with a mind map to get your visionary creative juices flowing. Draw bubbles branching ideas off of this circle for how this world would work, with pictures of your ideas inside the bubbles. This is a great exercise to do as a team or group. Go through a day in the life of a person in this world and where applicable, start writing out the answers to the questions below.

3. Functions: How will it work? What products do people use in their daily life? What will the machines do? What will the political structure be? What will the financial structure be? What are the people like? What will the parties and social gatherings be like? What will the art look like? How will the roads, food, schools, and shopping malls be different in your new world?

4. Senses: What does it visually look like? What will make it beautiful? What will it feel like? What will it smell like? What does it sound like when you walk down the street?

5. Emotions: What emotions do you get when you think of this world? What kind of energy does it have? What meaning does it have? How will people treat each other and relate to each other?

6. You: Who would *you* be in this world? How will your life improve? Remember, you are the one creating this new world, so the person *you become* in this world can be a motivating force for you.

7. Written phrases: Write down five or more phrases that convey what this world is like.

8. Decorate your space: Put pictures of your mind maps, mood boards, illustrations, and vision phrases around your work space to make this vision feel possible.

TIP: You can meditate before doing this exercise to create the mental space for the ideas and vision to germinate. You can hire an illustrator to capture your vision and use the artwork in your branding and marketing material.

STEP #4

IDEA STORM

"Ideas are not like fine china, ideas are like paper cups—they are cheap to manufacture, and when one has holes in it, go get another one." — Jesse Schell, *The Art of Game Design*

Now that you've fleshed out your visualization of the beautiful future from the last chapter, it should be thick with rich and beautiful ideas. Start listing the ideas you see in your mind map and sketches. Your task now is to write down 100 ideas that will help take your cause from the current world today to your future visualization of tomorrow. Look at your data goal again, and ask the question, *"How do we get there?"* There's something about putting data at the center of your creative process that ignites the imagination. It will help you generate lots of great ideas that are fresh and different—probably too many! Think of it as *harvesting ideas* from looking deeply into your data.

Coming up with 100 ideas is crazy, you say? Here's the thing—trying to get to 100 ideas will make you dig deep into your creativity. Don't worry if your ideas seem silly or seem like science fiction. Often the best idea will be buried the deepest. Ideas are like layers of an onion. As you peel away one layer of an idea, you'll be able to see the next idea. Once you are 20 ideas in, you have lifted off the obvious ideas and you'll need to make new mental connections and think in different ways to get to the next layer below. The kind of ideas you'll come up with when you are 90 ideas in will be quite different from your fifth idea.

As soon as I started using this process, I started having the best ideas I've ever had, and the more I think like this, the better it gets. I'd like to see you have so many ideas that you are giving them away like a grandmother next door with a tree that produces so much fruit that she gives boxes of oranges to everyone on the street.

There is a Japanese philosophy called *kaizen* which can be roughly translated to *continual improvement*. It means finding ways to always improve a system or to always optimize a workflow, instead of remaining rigid and unchanging. Employing *kaizen* means allowing your ideas to be always improving, flowing, and changing. It means continually assessing your ideas and systems to see how effectively they are shifting the dial on your data, and with this sentiment, you make small changes every day to do it better.

Let's not forget though, that ideas are not always your friend. Ideas can even be dangerous. Maybe you have at one point had a really good idea, but then realized later on that it was actually a pretty bad idea. I've done that—many times. It's possible that your *current idea* might be suffocating new and *better ideas* from coming through. We could even argue that getting attached to a single idea is a *liability* to the imagination.

Be wary of getting hooked into thinking there is *one special idea* out there for you that will blossom into the startup of your dreams and change the world. Ideas are abundant. *Ideas are free.* There is no tangible limit to how fruitful your capacity to invent new ideas can be. Ideas are like stars in the sky that light the way —they *facilitate* your journey to reach your goal data point. Ideas are not endpoints in themselves. Think of the problem you are trying to solve as the trunk of a tree, with thousands of ideas exploding out like acorns. Ideas, like acorns, will fall to the ground and some will grow and some won't, but the tree will always make new ones.

Don't be shy about embracing your craziest ideas. Go deeper. A fantasy idea like "water-powered flying cars" might be the stepping stone to your next idea that *is* viable. Maybe it's not flying cars, but it gets you to think about *underground* cars, and then about underground bike tunnels. You contact Elon Musk's *Boring Company* (they bore tunnels for underground transportation) and

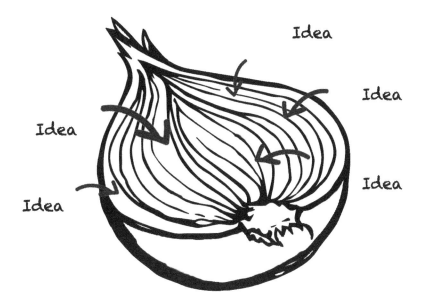

Ideas are layers of the onion: each idea you come up with will reveal another idea beneath. Keep pushing to come up with more ideas and peeling away the layers. The more layers you peel away, the better your ideas will be.

start working on a plan to bore a bike path tunnel from the Golden Gate Bridge through a very steep mountain to Marin City, that currently makes bike commuting almost impossible. One day that bike tunnel might happen, or your pursuit of it at least spark a movement of bike tunnel designs in cities around the world.

Your crazy fantasy idea led to a reasonably viable idea, and if that idea doesn't happen, the process of exploring the "crazy idea" will probably illuminate a dozen even better viable ideas. I've often been shy about pursuing my craziest ideas, but when I have done so (often years after I thought them up) I discovered that after a couple of months working on my idea, it didn't seem crazy anymore. I find that other people in the world are working on something related, and it all starts to seem perfectly logical. The holy grail of innovation is in exercising your brain to continually invent many, many ideas.

If you ever have a choice to hold back and choose the safe vanilla option or dive into your wildest ideas, go for the wild one. It's a no-brainer. The world craves inspiration. It craves novelty. It craves innovation. You will most likely find some corner of your wildest ideas that has real viability and can light up the world.

Choose a measurable destination for your goal, and draw on your visualization to mind-map at least 100 ideas of how to reach this number.

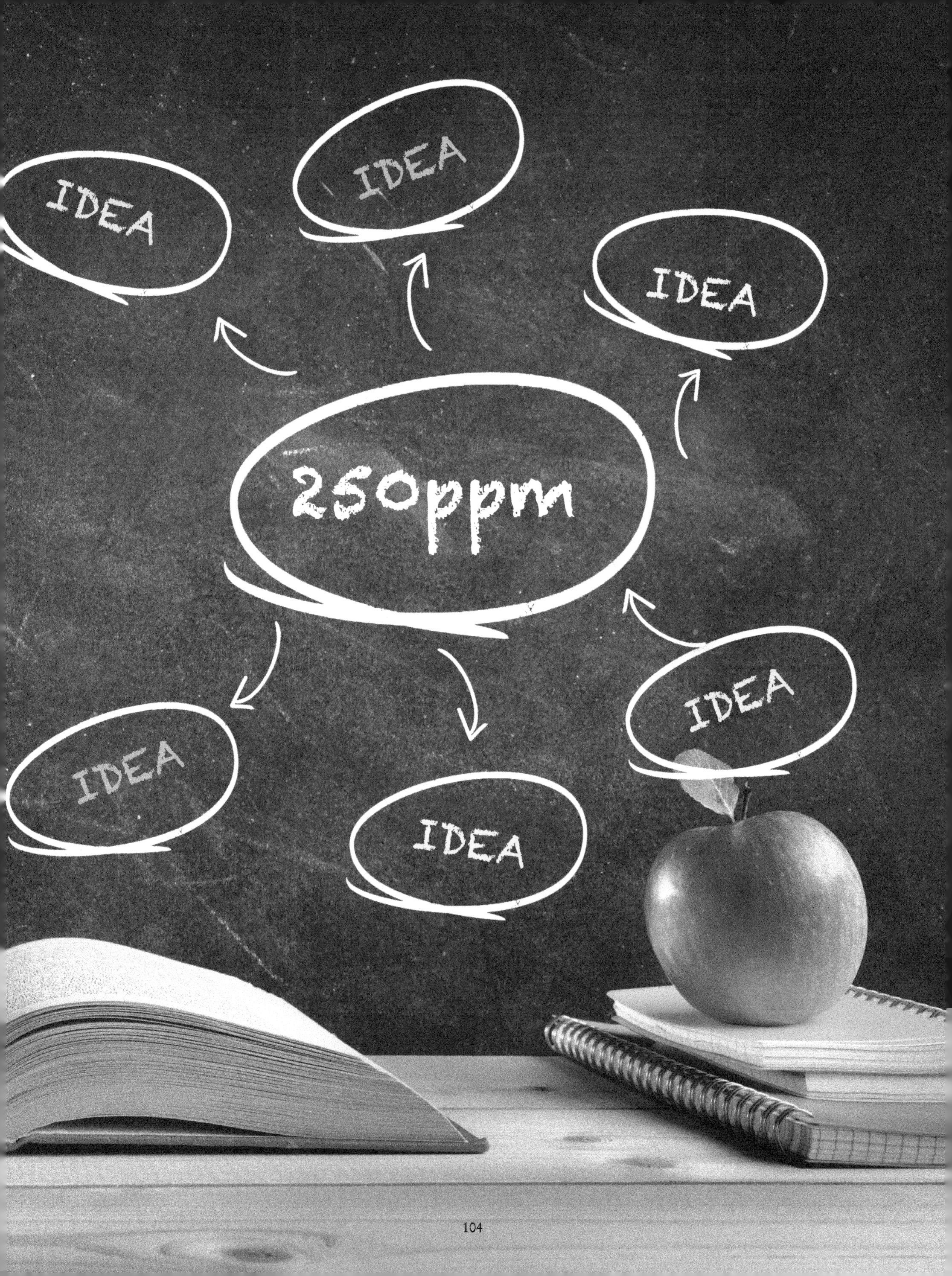
IDEA
IDEA
IDEA
250ppm
IDEA
IDEA
IDEA

HOW TO HAVE BETTER IDEAS

Imagine a local sustainability festival. It's a typical event that happens once a year where vendors congregate in stalls, there are keynote speakers, some food vendors, and lots of local people passing through.

If you remember the *Value-Action Gap*, it's likely that an event like this falls smack bang in the middle of it. Don't forget that as a strategy to change the world, an event is *just an idea*. If the event organizers are so attached to *the idea* of a festival, they might be closed to the process of germinating new and even better ideas. It doesn't mean anyone needs to do away with events or annual festivals altogether, but big events do need to be reconstructed in a way that continually drives people to not just experience the event, but also *adopt behaviors* to shift the numbers on a cause.

Imagine we ask the festival organizers, *"What do we want to change in the world?"* and then *"What metric can we use to measure this change?"* The organizing team can then look deeply into available datasets on the issue and start brainstorming. The team decides they want to focus on food sustainability as their central cause. They do some research and look deeper into the numbers and find there are a few different ways of measuring food sustainability. They come up with a list of these data sets:

➢ Food waste going to landfill (pounds per day)
➢ Composting (yes/no for households)
➢ Plastic packaging (pounds purchased per day)
➢ Pesticide use (pounds per year)
➢ Water use (megalitres per day)
➢ Fossil fuels used in farming (gallons per year)
➢ Industrial animal agriculture (number of animals grown per month)
➢ Food grown within 100 miles (square feet of land used for local food growing)

That's a lot of metrics! The team has a brainstorming session and they think through ways they can impact these numbers from within their local community, while also utilizing their event management skills. By letting go of their attachment to the idea of their annual sustainability festival, and focusing instead on measurements, they come up with these new ideas:

➢ Get people to grow more food locally.
➢ Give out stickers and signs that people can put on their trash to
   help remind them to put food waste in the compost bin.

HARVEST IDEAS FROM LOOKING DEEP INTO YOUR DATA

Ideas should fall like acorns
from your tree of data.

> Lobby local government to do compost pickups from homes and businesses.
> Make data about food waste in the local landfill available publicly on the internet.
> Recruit schools and businesses to help reduce food waste.
> Hold a DIY composting class for locals.
> Give out free calico bags for people to buy plastic-free bulk foods.
> Hold classes in food gardening.

As the team keeps coming up with more ideas, the organizers realize that what they *really need* is not a generic annual festival, but a *specific* monthly event. They need a monthly event that builds a community movement towards a sustainable local food system and has clear actions that people can take. They realize the monthly events need to take the form of classes and workshops that teach people skills (and of course *behaviors*) in zero-waste living, home food growing, and composting. They come up with a whole new targeted mission that manifests in this quantitative mission statement,

"Our mission is to have 50 percent of our city's food grown locally."

In order to make this quantitative goal come true, the organizers are going to have to determine the current surface area allocated to local food gardens and urban agriculture. They get their members to let them know where all the food gardens are, and plot them out on Google Maps, then calculate the current surface area used for food growing. They figure out how much land space it would take to reach their goal of 50 percent of the city's food grown locally. Now they know where their measurements are *today*, and what they want their organization to achieve *tomorrow*. They print out a copy of the map, with all the local food gardens highlighted in bright green.

Data is an excellent way to motivate people. They show the map to people in the community and say something like this: *"We need to bring our local food growing from 12,430 square feet up to 150,000 square feet. Could you help us reach this goal? Please come to our food growing monthly meetup. Our community offers garden blitzes where we can help you build a food garden."* The sustainability festival has now been reinvented into a community movement that is focused on driving measurable change. The organizers change the name from the generic "Sustainability Festival" to "Growing Local" to reflect their new focus on food and measurable change. The program now runs all year long and consists of the ideas across the page on the notepad.

With all these new ideas in play, the organization's mission changes from creating an *event* to creating a *movement* (that includes events). The team is

Idea storm: getting to 50% food locally grown

1. Monthly public meetups that showcase and teach food sustainability actions.
2. A website that shows maps of food gardens and data about local food sustainability metrics.
3. An online training website that has courses and video tutorials that teach food growing, composting, and sustainable living.
4. Local gardening blitz group that helps people establish new gardens and learn from others.
5. People can gather points by helping with gardening blitzes. Points can be redeemed for gardening support by the community. There's a prize at the end of the year for the person with the most points.
6. Annual awards night party where top food gardeners and volunteers are given awards and prizes.
7. An annual house and garden tour where newbies can be shuttled around to visit the city's best food gardens to learn from others and get advice from community leaders.
8. The surface area of local food gardens is tracked and displayed on an online map with a progress bar showing how far the city has to go to reach its food sustainability goal.
9. Top food growers, the Mayor, and local leaders holding their home-grown produce are professionally photographed and shared on social media and local press.
10. A sticker is given out to homes to put on letter boxes and publicly visible places to identify the house as a friend of the mission towards a sustainable food city.
11. Make it officially part of the city identity. A sign in a local park is put up that says "City Name - *The local food city.*"
12. Task force pushes local government to add more community gardens and urban orchards to city parks.
13. Establish a help line for roof top gardening advice and sell an easy and inexpensive garden starter kit.

Ideas for measurable change: a mock-up website for the example of a generic sustainability festival reinvented to measurably change the amount of food grown locally. This design features a map with data, a progress bar based on total square feet of local food gardens, and a call to action to invite people to start their own food garden.

devoted to the primary objective of figuring out how to increase the surface area for locally grown food. Every month, and every year, they keep mapping the surface area, sharing the maps, and building community momentum to reach their quantitative goal.

What's the happy ending? The community is injected with excitement and positivity. People are making new social connections, learning new skills, and everyone is inspired because they are seeing real and tangible change happen every month. This wouldn't be possible if the event organizers were so attached to their original idea of the annual festival that they couldn't grow into a new strategy. Let your ideas go and invent new ones as quickly and easily as the speed of thought. Remember, the only idea that really matters is the one that shifts the numbers.

STEP #4: IDEA STORM EXERCISE

1. Write out your ideas: Look through your visualization exercise from Chapter Three and start writing out the ideas you generated.

2. 100 ideas: Write 100 ideas for what the world your visualized needs to function. Write ideas for how you will reach your goal numbers. You ideas can be anything from simple behaviors to science fiction technology. Keep your mental energy flowing around the problem. Keep asking yourself, *"How could this new world work?"*

3. Make branches for different sectors: If you get stuck for ideas, try making categories or branches for different industries, types of people, or market sectors. Start exploring branches such as food, transportation, social life, babies, clothing, e-waste, education and whatever else you can think of. Keep branching and coming up with more ideas.

Beware of stopping early

Don't flake out on this exercise at just a few ideas. Don't stop at 27 ideas. Keep going. You're one diamond of an idea could come to you at idea 88. Your ideas can even be indirect. You might write down an idea for an app, then you write down something next to it like, *"I really need to enroll in a course to learn how to code."* You enroll in a course and there you meet a project partner and together you make a start-up that changes the world for a totally separate idea.

A little story: I started having pretty wild ideas once I learned to think like this, and I was shy to work on them because I thought they were too "out there," but I finally just bit the bullet and went for it. People loved my crazy ideas. Once you've put a few puzzle pieces together, and answered some hard questions, your crazy ideas become a reasonable and practical approach to a significant problem. Don't pull away from your craziest ideas. Go deeper into them.

DEVELOPMENT

BRAND EXPLORATION

Essen

Values &
Character

STEP #5

IDEA EVALUATION

"Throughout history, objective truth has been an exotic idea." — Steven Pinker, Harvard University Professor

To make sure you don't spend a chunk of your life working on an idea that just isn't effective at shifting your cause, you need to apply a systematic approach to choosing ideas *that will*. Don't choose ideas because they are emotionally compelling, cool, or buzz-word dense. Choose them because they *will work*, and work in a way that you can *measure.*

You need to create a system that assigns a unit of "effort" (usually money) per unit of impact. By shrewdly evaluating each of your ideas as to its potential to make a measurable impact, you can easily discard less effective ideas in favor of more effective ideas. You want to choose the ideas that are going to give the best bang for your buck that can keep feeding your upward spiral. This is the principle of *kaizen* in motion—to be in a continual state of evaluation, measurement and improvement.

Get your list of ideas from Chapter Four and give each idea a score from one to ten as to how hard or expensive the idea is going to be. Then in a second column, give the idea a score from one to ten as to the idea's propensity to reach your goal data point. If you can figure out the *cost per unit of influence*, such as $5.32 per ton of carbon dioxide saved, or $17.20 per acre of forest protected, this number will give you the best evaluation of the idea's worthiness. It might be difficult to figure out these numbers in detail, so start with an estimate out of ten.

Get a large piece paper or a spreadsheet and map out all your ideas with *impact* on the X-axis, and *cost* on Y-axis. You should see a trend in how your ideas scatter on your chart. Look at the ideas that are coming up in the quadrant of *low cost* and *high impact*—you can see it in the example chart with the green smiley face. These

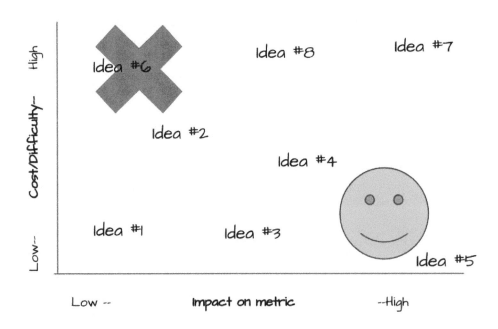

Give your ideas a value metric: chart your ideas by impact vs cost. Don't pursue ideas that have a low impact and are expensive that fall in the red X region. Choose ideas that have a high impact on your data and are inexpensive, that fall in the green smiley face region.

When it comes to changing the world, an idea is only a hypothesis.

are the ideas on which you want to focus. There should be one or more ideas showing up in this quadrant that look particularly inspiring.

There's a great perk to this rational and data-driven approach. Have you ever had someone on your team who keeps pushing a bad idea, but he or she has such a big voice that they steam-roll everyone into going along with it? Computer scientist Grace Hopper said, *"One accurate measurement is worth 1,000 expert opinions."* This idea-evaluation process will help water down anyone's annoying pet projects that are draining resources and not getting you closer to your goal. The numbers will objectively show the idea's potential without it needing to get personal.

You might notice that some of your own pet ideas or long-held dreams turn up not showing strong potential for making much measurable impact. You might also see that some dull ideas have big potential. If you *really* want to measurably change the world, you may need to focus on less glamorous ideas that shift the numbers in a bigger way. But don't shy away from an idea just because it doesn't look cool on the outside. Unglamorous ideas can reveal a silver lining, and turn out to be the more interesting ones in the end.

Imagine you've had a dream of starting a fabulous vegan food festival. It seems like it would be fun, you love food, and you'd be able to connect with people you've admired for years. You try to work out the score for the amount of effort required, and impact the festival would make on the pounds of meat eaten. You realize, when trying to quantify the *actual* amount of meat that the festival would take out of the supply chain, that it probably wouldn't take out much at all. You realize that most of the people who will go to the festival will already be eating a vegan diet. But you realize one very important thing—if you want to turn the world vegan, the last thing you should be doing is speaking with more vegans. To reduce the demand for meat, you have to find meat eaters, and inspire them to join the plant-based party. Your efforts will make measurable success, even if you only get meat-eaters to cut back on meat a little bit.

In your idea-storm you write down that McDonalds could, at the very least, mix a little soy protein into their burgers to make them lower in meat content. You calculate some quick numbers and realize that this idea, if successful, would have a *huge effect* on the amount of animals killed every week. It doesn't sound as much

> "One accurate measurement is worth 1,000 expert opinions."
> —Grace Hopper

fun as working on a festival, and what vegan wants to work with a meat-centric fast food corporation when she could be working with kindred spirit vegan chefs?

But if it works, you'd know *for sure* that you would have saved millions of animals' lives, and millions of tons of greenhouse gases from warming the planet. It may even be a critical stepping stone that topples the tipping point of major food retailers offering higher percentages of plant-based meat replacement products. Your idea gets global press coverage. It could truly be a revolution.

When working on urbancanopy.io, which is intended to reduce urban heat islands, I wanted to promote green roofs and green walls because I absolutely adore them. But during my research, I learned that getting people to paint their roofs white and installing energy efficient air conditioners was the most immediate means of bringing down peak summer electricity use. I'm really *not* in love with, and am never going to be in love with, white roof paint and energy efficient air conditioning units. I was a little crestfallen when I realized that if I wanted to shift the numbers, I had to shift the focus of my project away from beautiful, lush, eco-futuristic green walls and green roofs, and towards white paint and AC.

But I went with it, and it turns out that white roofing and AC have significant corporations behind them, like 3M, Dow Chemical, Panasonic, and GE, that could sponsor the pilot project. I discovered a whole new area of science in reflectance that can be calculated from satellite imagery and a realm of computer science I didn't know about before. I still get to promote green walls, too. If I had gotten trapped in my own idea-bias of just doing what I thought was appealing instead of following the numbers, I would have had a much smaller hobby-sized project, with less influence, or perhaps no project at all.

Every idea is only as good as its ability to create measurable change. If you can't prove that your idea is capable of changing the numbers, kill it off, and come up with a new idea that does. Don't worry if you were emotionally attached to it. Follow the breadcrumb of numbers through the forest of competing ideas and let them tell you the story of where you need to go.

APPLY THE SCIENTIFIC METHOD

When it comes to changing the world, an *idea is only a hypothesis.* Because we're in the game of *really* changing the world (not fake-changing the world, like *Peace Fare guy from page 171*), you need to make sure that your project does just that—it changes things. How can you tell if it's working? You need to set up the systems that check if your hypothesis (your idea) is actually shifting the numbers on what you want to change. You need to embed *the scientific method* into your design—and this includes a hypothesis, evidence that shows the hypothesis was true, and of course, a way to *measure* it.

How to design the scientific method into your social-change project:

Problem: What is the problem you are trying to change in the world?

Data: How are you measuring this problem, in real world data?

Hypothesis: What is your hypothesis of why you think your idea will affect this issue?

Evidence: How will you show evidence that your hypothesis is working? How will you measure its progress?

Causal mechanism: What is the causal mechanism for why it will work to create change?

Test it: Test your hypothesis with real humans in the leanest way possible to see if it works.

An easier way: Have you over-engineered the solution? Are there easier or cheaper ways to create this same change?

Think of your journey into world-changing as a practice into *experiment design.* Each iteration of your idea (or "pivot" as they are called in the startup world) and of your hypothesis is an alteration to your experiment. You should always be adjusting and reinventing your experiment to maximize a result, and weaving this kind of experiment design through any technology you build. A great project will show *evidence* that it's working to shift the numbers, and you'll need a crystal clear understanding of the causal link that drives the change.

HOW TO TEST IT

Turn your project into a lean behavioral science lab. Figure out the easiest and cheapest version of an experiment you can design that gathers evidence about whether your idea is going to work. Before investing thousands of hours, or even millions of dollars on a project that has no concrete evidence that it is going to deliver the change you want, test it. There are several ways you can do small petri-dish style tests on your ideas and designs. You don't need to have a big and well-funded project to test a hypothesis. Even if you are designing a flyer that asks people to compost, you can test out some different combinations of words, colors, and images on thirty people. Here are a few ways you can test your project:

Amazon Mechanical Turk: Have you ever had a design or an idea for something and shown it around to a few people for feedback? There's a more robust way to do it. You can use Amazon Mechanical Turk at mturk.com to show your designs and surveys to hundreds or even thousands of people for a price of about five cents per respondent.

Mailbox Drop: If you are seeking a response from people, drop three batches to demographically similar households, each with 100 letters showing different designs, with a call line and web-sign-up offer. See which version gets the best results.

Facebook and Google ads: Test variations of your idea and messages using advertisements on Facebook or Google before you start your project or startup. You can test several concepts with the same audience preferences and see which one gets the best traction.

Classroom of students: Put your design or project in front of a class of students and watch or document how they respond.

Conference or festival: Try signing people up to your idea, or asking for feedback from people at a conference or festival related to the area of your project, before you build it out too far.

STEP #5: EVALUATION EXERCISE

1. Score the impact potential of your ideas: You should now have a list of about 100 ideas. Go through each of your ideas and give them a rank out of 10 as to how likely the idea is to shift the numbers on your cause. You can do it simply by giving your ideas an A, B, or C, or you can also take an advanced approach and investigate the quantitative impact each idea will have.

2. Score the cost of each of your ideas: Give each idea a number out of 10 as to how difficult or expensive the idea will be to implement.

3. Assign a value metric: Determine a singular guiding metric that takes the shape of "cost per unit of impact" for each of your ideas, or the closest you can get. It might look like "dollars per megaliter of water saved," or "dollars per ton of compost kept out of landfill."

4. Rank your ideas: Rank your ideas in order of your value metric, from the most effective idea to your least effective idea.

5. Shortlist your favorite ideas and choose one: Make a shortlist of your ideas that will have a high impact on your goal and have a low cost to implement. Out of these ideas, choose the one idea, or a small number of ideas, that you want to work on.

Tip
Be careful to be disciplined to assess your ideas by the merits of their direct influence on your data. You might have one idea that is likely to have a large effect on your numbers, but is not very glamorous. You also never know where an unglamorous idea will take you. It may open up a whole range of opportunities, funding sources, and new connections.

STEP #6

BEHAVIOR CHANGE

"Your job isn't to build more software faster: it's to maximize the outcome and impact you get from what you choose to build." — Jeff Patton, *User Story Mapping*

It's easy to view the causes we work on as features of the *physical world*, such as a tree being cut down, or a chemical leaching into a river. Of course, these problems are real, but these physical manifestations are *symptoms*—they are symptoms of *human actions*. That means we have the difficult job of figuring out how to actually get many humans to take different actions.

All change is ultimately behavior change. Approaching the problem you are trying to solve as a *behavioral scientist,* rather than an *activist,* is quite possibly the most important step you can take, yet it's frequently overlooked, and we can't change the world without this approach.

You need to take care to move your project away from an *education*-centric focus that runs the risk of falling down the Value-Action Gap and into a *behavior*-centric approach. This means that, instead of making projects that teach people about the importance of an issue, you need to look carefully at the discrete *actions* you want to encourage, and design a highly specific solution that will make people do that thing.

For example, instead of *only* teaching a group of people about carbon dioxide emissions and melting glaciers, you give each person in your group a light (like meetglow.com) that changes color based on their energy usage, or one of the energy-saving apps such as Chai Energy, Sense, or Bidgely. You give them the light for free, but the students need to pay a small price to get it—they each need to write a statement that says something like, *"I pledge to reduce my energy use for the next 30 days"* on a piece of paper. You can photograph each student holding that piece of paper in one hand and the energy light in the other, then print all the photos out and put them on a wall somewhere public, like a hallway wall.

Thirty days later everyone checks back in and compares how successful they were at cutting down their energy consumption. You rank your students on a leaderboard with the most energy saved at the top, and the least energy saved on the bottom. You give the winner a gold star and a box of organic chocolates, but more importantly, you get the other students to give the winner a round of applause. You don't need to give up on education—you can hold a lecture on glaciers, too—but knowledge about glaciers is probably not the thing that will make people *act*. You can see from this example how different this approach between *education* and *behavior* is. Your ideas will take a refreshingly different, more fun, and more *effective* shape with behavior-centric thinking.

1		2		3
Actor	->	Action	->	Result

Actor, action, result: identify your types of actors, the one very specific action you want them to take, and the measurable result this action will have on your cause.

ACTOR, ACTION, & MEASUREMENT

The first stepping stone of working out how to change a human's behavior is to identify these three things:

Actor: Your target person.
Action: What you want the person to do.
Measurement: The measurable effect his or her action will have on your goal.

It might look simple, but figuring out these three things grants a power that many projects lack. Get started by identifying your *actor*. This is the person you are trying to influence. It could be a few different types of people. It could be an ordinary person, CEO, judge, politician, new mother, car buyer, procurement manager, or a fellow student at your school. I like to get a big piece of paper and draw a stick figure of the actor or actors.

The second step is to decide on the one *action* you want this person to do. The action could be something like composting, riding a bike, or approving a city ordinance. It doesn't matter what the action is, as long as there is one type of person engaging in one specific action.

The third step is to write down the *measurable result* that occurs when your actor takes this action. If you are asking the person to cut down on plastic, to compost more, or to ride their bike, you need to know exactly, in numbers of real-world matter, what the result is going to be.

When I asked these questions for the *V-score* app (see the behavior map later in this chapter), I identified three main actors: restaurant owners, people wanting to eat out, and volunteers who'd help enter the menu data into the app. Each of these actors does a different action: restaurant owners switch their ingredients from animal products to plant-based, hungry people discover high V-score restaurants, and volunteers can easily calculate new V-scores for more eateries. Each actor needed a user interface design that worked for his or her needs, and it all needed to happen within the same app. Identifying these actions separately for the three types of actors provided the fundamental skeleton design of the app.

DE-CLUSTERING BEHAVIORS

When you are working out the actions you want your actors to do, at first the behavior you are thinking about is probably actually *several behaviors* clustered together. Your target action might be something like *go vegan, cut down on electricity,* or *cut back on plastic,* but when you think about it, each of these behaviors actually consists of several different sub-behaviors, a bit like a large branch that has smaller branches growing from.

We need to be careful of asking people to do too many actions, using messages that cluster too many behaviors together. This mistake robs you of the nuance required to create the kind of *very specific* behavior-change prompts it takes to affect a single behavior. A project targeting a specific behavior such as helping people remember their reusable water bottles is going to take a different form than a project designed to get people to use shampoo bars instead of plastic bottled shampoo. They both say "Use less plastic" but the location, products, and action needed are totally different. When it comes to changing behavior, less is more.

De-clustering is a process of reducing your target behavior into the simplest possible sub-behaviors until there are no variations on the behavior left (read Doug McKenzie Mohr's book, *Fostering Sustainable Behavior* for more detail on this). Let's look at the example of composting. At first glance, it might seem like asking people to compost (or just throw their food scraps into a green bin) is just *one* behavior. But when we look into it and de-cluster it, we can see that composting actually consists of a few different behaviors that happen in different locations.

Sub-behaviors of composting might include:

1) Composting at home when you have a garden
2) Composting at work
3) Composting at the mall
4) Composting on an outdoor shopping street
5) Composting at a café
6) Composting at home in an apartment

There are probably even more variations to composting than this, but as you can see, through the de-clustering process, we've already turned one composting behavior into six different composting sub-behaviors. Each of these sub-behaviors needs its own equally unique behavior-change strategy. Getting cafés to compost will become an entirely different campaign than getting people who live in small apartments to compost on their balconies. Getting workplaces in the city to

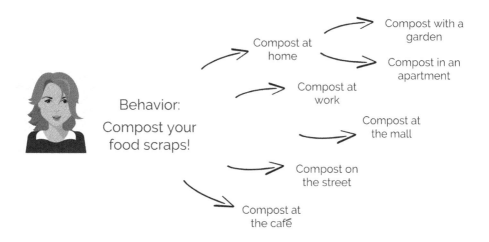

Behavior:
Compost your
food scraps!

Compost at
home

Compost with a
garden

Compost in an
apartment

Compost at
work

Compost at
the mall

Compost on
the street

Compost at
the café

De-clustering behaviors: the one thing you want people to do can often be broken down into many things, each of which needs its own strategy. Your task is to reduce your target behavior into as many sub-behaviors as possible until you can't simplify them any more.

compost will be an entirely different project than getting people who are walking down a shopping strip to put an apple core in a public green bin.

If you are finding that you have a lot of actors, and many actions, don't be shy about narrowing your project's focus. If your goal is to get your whole city (or even the whole world!) to quit using plastic, narrow down your type of actor, and perhaps focus on one strip of restaurants on one street. Instead of asking a restaurant to give up *all* disposable plastic, start by asking for only one discrete action—to quit plastic straws. Instead of starting a project called *"Plastic-free Melbourne"* (many actors and many actions) you narrow your campaign and call it *"Straw-Free Gertrude Street"* (one actor and one action). Melbourne's artsy Gertrude Street has only about ten restaurants you need to convince to do one thing. It's an achievable goal. Getting traction with one small project will set an example for others to follow—and people *love* to copy what others are already doing. Once you have one success, then move to the next street, and on to the next, until your movement is snowballing.

The next step is to quantify the measurable impact your sub-behaviors will have on the data you are trying to change. Work out which sub-behavior will make the greatest measurable impact, and focus on the one that makes the most measurable change.

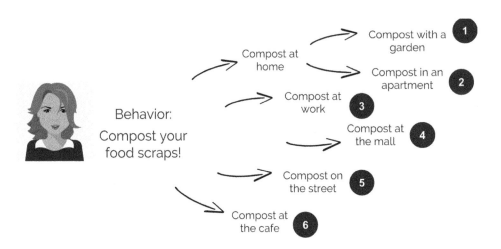

De-clustering behaviors: the simple action of composting food scraps can be broken down into six different sub-behaviors, which each need a different campaign design. It's best to choose one sub-behavior, and do it thoroughly until you see measurable change, rather than spread your resources thin and get little traction on all the behaviors.

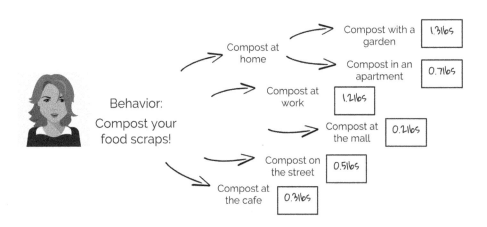

Measurable impact of behaviors: write down an estimate for how each behavior could affect the numbers. Then you can choose a single sub-action to focus on that will bring about the most measurable change.

USER STORY MAPPING

User story mapping is a world-changer's best friend. It's a common practice in software development but rarely used in environmental or social change projects. This is a tragedy because a user story mapping exercise will illuminate exactly how you will be able to influence the people you are trying to influence, and at what time and place throughout their day. I can't get excited enough about this practice. Every time I do a user story mapping workshop, the process has turned the project into something vastly better than the original idea we started with. It involves answering three main questions — and these questions change everything.

1. Who is the target person?
2. How will the target person initially hear about, or see your product or message?
3. What is the thing they will do after they see your product or message that will make measurable change happen?

You should have identified your key actors from the previous exercise and what action you want them to take. Start by drawing a stick figure of each actor and write down their name. Then ask the second question, *"How will they hear about it?"* This question will sculpt the shape of your project in a big way when you ask it *first* before planning anything else. Will they get an email invite? Will they see it on social media? Will they see a colored sticker on an item for purchase? Will they see it on a public screen? Will they get a letter in the mail? Then consider what reaction people will have once they see it. What will they do? Draw the steps each actor goes through during their day. They wake up in the morning, then what do they do? What do they do next? Keep drawing the steps they take throughout their whole day, to the very end point when they take the action you want them to take.

The results from user story mapping can be astonishing. In a couple of hours of drawing out the behaviors of stick figures, you can give your project a complete strategic reinvention. What comes out of your map often doesn't make the project cost more, it just makes it better.

The University of Santa Cruz asked me to build some software that would take the waste data they were collecting from their on-campus garbage trucks and put it on charts on the internet. They wanted the charts to update automatically, as the garbage trucks moved about. I could have just done that and thought nothing more about it. But being obsessed about influencing real human beings to make real change, I started the user story mapping exercise with the team. The first question I asked was, *"Who are we trying to influence?"* *"The students"* they replied. I didn't know from the project brief that the target audience was the

Example of user story mapping for the Vscore app

The Vscore app shows the ratio of plant-to-animal foods in a restaurant's menu. Its aim is to nudge restaurants to use less meat, dairy, and eggs, and more plant-based ingredients. This is a map of the movements of the app's three main types of users: restaurant owner/chef, hungry person looking to eat, and volunteers helping to input menu data. This map provides the skeleton for the user interaction design.

Step 1: How will a restaurant owner or chef first discover it?

Step 2: Find my restaurant

Step 3a: See my score

Step 3b: No Vscore yet? Add yours now

User type 1: Restaurant owner / chef

Step 1: How will a hungry person first discover it?

Step 2: See the Vscores of restaurants near you

Step 3a: See a map of Vscores by color spots

Step 3b: Filter by > 75% Vscore

User type 2: Hungry person searching for a low-meat meal

Step 1: How will a volunteer first discover it?

Step 2a: Do you have restaurant you want to add?

Step 3: Add food items to form

User type 3: Volunteer helping to add new menu data to the app

Step 2b: Or would you like us to give you a menu that needs calculating?

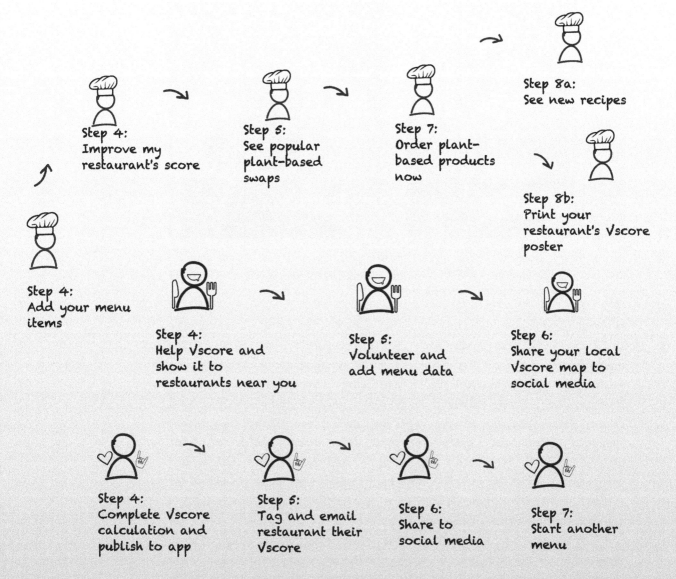

Step 4:
Improve my restaurant's score

Step 5:
See popular plant-based swaps

Step 7:
Order plant-based products now

Step 8a:
See new recipes

Step 8b:
Print your restaurant's Vscore poster

Step 4:
Add your menu items

Step 4:
Help Vscore and show it to restaurants near you

Step 5:
Volunteer and add menu data

Step 6:
Share your local Vscore map to social media

Step 4:
Complete Vscore calculation and publish to app

Step 5:
Tag and email restaurant their Vscore

Step 6:
Share to social media

Step 7:
Start another menu

A user story map (or behavior map) is a fundamental exercise to help illustrate the exact behavior you want to influence, where the behavior happens, and what options each user can take. Do a user story map *before* you start any project or design. Build your project up around supporting, motivating, and prompting this key action. If you are building an app, this map will provide the structure of your user interface design.

Vscore: An app that shows the ratio of plant-to-animal foods in a restaurant's menu, with the aim of nudging restaurants to offer more plant-based options and reduce their habit of including meat, dairy, and eggs in most meals.

students. No one would have told me if I had not asked. That changed everything.

The second question I asked was, *"How will they see it or hear about it?"* No one had a good answer. Will they open a smartphone app to check on the campus's waste data? Probably not. Will they go and look at it via the university website? Probably not. Can we email the students every week through the university email system? Perhaps. Looking at the physical environment where the students roam, I suggested that we install a touch-screen in the dorms that showed the waste data on a leaderboard. That way the students can't avoid seeing it. The team seemed pretty excited about this idea. The third big question was, *"What action will the students need to take in order to change the numbers?"* We identified a handful of zero waste actions that would be most impactful.

In three short questions, we turned the project from what was going to be an infographic on the web, into something far better—a beautiful touch screen interface in a lovely laser-cut wooden kiosk enclosure; a zero waste training guide; and a zero waste email course—all for about the same cost as building a few web-based infographics. Adding a little bit of structure to the creative process can lead to wonderful things.

You may need to create several behavior maps for your different audiences, and also for each of the different behaviors you want them to do. Be patient and thorough with it. Don't worry though, user story maps are free. A detailed map can take several hours to do, but once you've done it, it will distill your ideas into a focused strategy that becomes the basis for your whole change-operation to come to life.

THE BEHAVIOR FUNNEL

If you've learned sales and marketing, you've probably come across the concept of *the funnel*. It also applies to environmental and social change behaviors. The funnel describes the process of reaching out to a group of people, representing the large top part of the funnel, and attempting to pull them through a process, and get as many people as possible out of that group to do the thing you want them to do, which means they pass through the small end of the funnel at the end.

If you're selling solar panels, getting someone successfully all the way through the funnel would mean that you've gotten a customer signed up, paid, and ready to put their solar panels on the roof. When it comes to behavior change, getting someone through the funnel means you've gotten them to take *an action*. The top of the funnel might be the number of people entering a coffee shop on a given day, say it's 500 people. The people who successfully make it through the funnel would be the number of people who bring their own reusable coffee cup in with them. This might be 71 people. This coffee cup funnel that succeeds in changing the behavior of 71 out of 500 people has a 14 percent success rate.

You can view your behavior map from the previous exercise as a funnel. Imagine that you have reached out to 1,000 people. These people might have seen your ad on Facebook, walked past your stand at a festival, received a letter from you in the mail, picked up your phone call, or it's the kids you see every day at school. You need to take these people through a series of steps that lead them to the final target behavior. It's like trying to get a mouse to move through a maze. Your job is to take a scientific approach to figure out how to get better at moving people from each phase of the funnel to the next.

Stephen Wendel, author of *Designing for Behavior Change*, describes the behavior funnel using the CREATE acronym. I've added an example of how you can apply these steps to a campaign designed to help people use less plastic:

Cue: How will you get the person's attention at the right time? *Put a sign on the front door, a reminder tag on the work bag, a sign on the fridge, a smartphone app could make a reminder sound, there could be a 30-day water bottle challenge star-chart on the wall.*

Reaction: What reaction do you want your person to have? *To see the reminder prompts, then get her reusable water bottle and fill it up.*

Environment: In what environment is this reaction happening? How can we use the environment to help? Is there anything in the environment that is making the behavior difficult? *We need to make sure the person owns at least one reusable water bottle.*

Action: What is the action we need the person to do? *Put the filled water bottle in her work bag.*

Timing: What time does this need to happen? *7.45 a.m. when she is leaving for work.*

Execute: What signifies the action has been executed? *The person leaves the house for work with their filled water bottle.*

Draw a picture of your behavior funnel and see if you can find any points where it might be leaking. How many people are getting into your behavior funnel? How many people make it out the other side and successfully complete the target behavior? What is your funnel's success ratio?

It might sound trivial to break up a simple action like leaving the house with a reusable water bottle down into these discrete steps, but by applying the CREATE formula, you will identify weaknesses where your funnel could be leaking, and it can also help you come up with new ideas to further enliven your campaign.

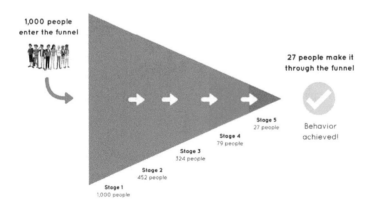

The behavior funnel: Your target behavior can be broken down into a series of sequential phases that your audience moves through. Your job is to get as many people as possible through the funnel and out the other side to complete the target behavior.

THE PHYSICAL ENVIRONMENT

Look closely at the movements a person makes in response to his or her physical environment. See where you can intervene in a way that makes a difference. People often struggle to do the right thing simply because the physical environment isn't set up to help them.

Think of The Great Bag-Remembering Dilemma. We all forget to bring our reusable bags to the store, at least sometimes. Get this—while there's a worldwide movement to end plastic bags, there is almost no movement whatsoever to help people *remember* their reusable bags. People need signs everywhere that say *"Have you remembered your bags?"* We need to have signs hanging on doorknobs, suctioned to car windows, and sticking out in parking lots. Why haven't Trader Joe's and The Sierra Club gotten together and distributed these kinds of prompts such as a door hanger sign packed inside every reusable bag I buy? Why aren't they given out for free at the cash register along with the cute flower stickers they give to my little girl?

We can make no-frills interventions in the physical space that have impressive results. I used to live in a communal house with twelve other people. With that many people living together, it was easy to see the unnecessary disposable paper bags accumulate quickly. They piled up, spilling out of drawers and cupboards everywhere. I could have told everyone how annoying it was, and that they all ought to try harder to use reusable bags. I knew if people were not using their reusable bags, it was a fault of the system we had in the house, not the people. We didn't have any system in the house for helping people take reusable bags to the store. I jumped on amazon.com and bought a coat hanger rack for $14.00 and installed it in the doorway. I hung all the reusable bags in our house on it, then got a white piece of paper and wrote *"Please remember your bags when you go shopping"* with a few love hearts and a smiley face. Immediately my house-mates started to remember their bags, and through my observations, I estimated disposable bag use went down by about three quarters. It didn't take an elaborate documentary, or anyone having an epiphany about the embodied energy of paper or plastic. It just took a rack of hooks from Amazon that required less than ten minutes to install, and having it positioned in the right place in the physical environment.

The world seems full of behavioral holes that can be easily patched. A couple of years ago I was shopping at San Francisco's bulk-food-utopia Rainbow Grocery and I wanted to buy reusable cloth produce bags—the small bags you use for loose pasta or oats. I was struggling to find them. They sell so many things in that store that cater to the deepest of deep hippies that it was crazy I couldn't figure out

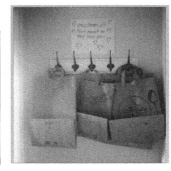

Simple interventions in the physical environment: Door hanger reminder signs, a bottle refill station, and a coat rack to hang reusable bags near the front door.

where to buy a simple cloth bag to put my tomatoes in. Finally, I asked a worker, but he didn't know either. He asked another worker. She didn't know. Then one of them went to the head office and after about ten minutes someone else came out finally and found the organic cotton produce bags. They were stuffed in a corner, on the *other side* of the store from the bulk foods section—and it's a big store.

Why weren't these bags placed front and center where all the bulk goods were? How many hundreds of people were peeling off plastic bags every hour (they are compostable corn-based plastic, but still) for the simple reason that no one at Rainbow Grocery had thought to prominently locate the reusable bags in the right place where people would buy them? A tiny alteration to the physical environment can, by default, save zillions of resources, taking hardly any effort at all.

Seat belts chimes are another good example of altering the immediate environment. You know how modern cars beep when you don't put your seatbelt on? It's a direct message that happens *right at the time and place* it matters—when you are sitting next to your seatbelt ready to click in. An advertisement that encourages seat-belt use on a billboard, the radio, or television, and even the threat of a police officer giving you a ticket does not occur at the time when you sit in the vehicle, and may not stay in the driver's mind long enough to influence him. The beep happens at the exact time and place when it needs to work, and if you don't click in your seatbelt, the system basically annoys you into putting it on.

Look through your behavior map and see if there are any easy interventions you can make to the physical environment. There could be several things you can do that can have big, exciting, and measurable results.

FOOT IN THE DOOR TECHNIQUE

Asking someone straight up to make a substantial change, donation, or commitment can backfire. Without giving people a few stepping stones they can use to get accustomed to the change, a big and sudden request usually results in a knee-jerk *"No!"* The person you want to influence shuts the door.

Imagine that you are planning to ask your parents to contribute something big, like $10,000 for you to take a course at a private college. You probably already intuitively know that if you pick up the phone and ask cold, *"Hey, could I have ten grand? It's for a thing that is really important to me,"* then your mother or father would probably yelp *"No! Jeez, are you serious?"* But if you set the conversation up gently and first ask the question, *"Can I talk to you about something I'd like to do?"* followed by *"Can you be open-minded about this thing I want to discuss with you?"* then you are asking for small incremental agreements first, or "little yesses" that set the conversation up for you to ask for the big thing.

We need to take the same approach when trying to get people to adopt environmental and social changes. It's called the *Foot in the Door Technique*. It means that getting someone to make a small change or commitment first primes them to make a larger change at a later time.

A well-known study on the *Foot in the Door Technique* involved asking homeowners to put up a sign in their front yard that said *"Drive Carefully."* One group of homeowners was asked to put up a very large version of the sign. Nearly all of these people declined. Another group of homeowners was asked to put up a very small version of the sign and this time, nearly all of these homeowners agreed to the small sign. Two weeks later, the researchers went back to visit the people who had agreed to put up the small sign and asked them if they would be interested in upgrading the size of their little sign to the really big sign. The result was astonishing. Seventy-six percent of homeowners who had previously been asked to post a small sign now agreed to put up the large sign in their yard.(1) Asking for a sudden big change shoots your prospect for change in the foot. Asking for a little change puts your foot in the door.

A modern application of the *Foot in the Door Technique* is the *Meat Free Monday* campaign. Before Meat Free Monday was established, plant-eating advocacy largely consisted of the *Go Vegan* message. It's quite likely that a demand to *"go vegan"* is akin to the previous example of asking a homeowner to put up a giant sign. The ask is too big, and so most people say no. A smaller ask, such as *"Go vegan only on Mondays"* is like the example of asking homeowners to put up the small sign. Most people agree.

Drive carefully: Foot in the Door Technique study from the YouTube channel "In 59 seconds."

Meat Free Monday has successfully signed up 80 schools in Scotland to take part in the program. This means that thousands of children are now introduced to plant-based meals every single week. The important message of eating more plants and fewer animals is also getting a foot in the door in the formative years of these children's education. It's a simple campaign that could easily be adopted in corporate cafeterias, schools, hospitals, hotels, and boardroom lunches all across the world.

Occasionally people who are passionate about a cause express a concern that these small asks will lull people into complacency, and end up enabling people to feel good about taking what they perceive as the easy way out. The recent trend of cities banning plastic straws has been criticized for putting too much weight behind a minuscule problem. But it's important to understand that each small ask does not dilute the whole movement's effectiveness. It actually *primes people* to make more substantial commitments later on.

Think of the *Foot in the Door Technique* as if you were creating a video game or a sport with a beginner level that you design to onboard newcomers to your movement. You introduce new people to a task or small challenge that is easy and helps get them started. Games usually have multiple levels. You can draw on this concept to keep offering new tasks to allow people to keep improving their skills and jumping from one level of skill to the next.

PLEDGES

Instead of hoping that the people you are trying to influence *might* make a change, you can cut to the chase and explicitly ask them to commit to a change. Our instinctual devotion to keeping a promise is strong, and we can use this psychological weight to get people to make a promise to the cause you are working on.

This promise is called a *pledge.* It is quite simply asking someone to commit to taking an action. You might ask someone to make a pledge such as *"I pledge to ride my bike to work once a week"* or *"I pledge to stop buying plastic-bottled drinks."* Pledges can be expressed in many forms. You can ask people to write down a pledge when they pass your market stall. You can prompt online users to fill out a pledge on your website. You can invite people to take a photo of themselves holding a piece of paper with their pledge handwritten on it, and then share these photos on your social media. You could get your city's mayor to sign a pledge on a formal certificate while being photographed by the local press.

Pledges are low-hanging fruit you can weave into your campaign. They are proven to deliver results and are easier than making elaborate educational brochures, videos, or apps. Pledges combine well with the *Foot in the Door Technique.* If you can get your most stubborn audiences to agree to make the

Pledges: Van Jones being photographed with a pledge from The Plastic Pollution Coalition. Public pledges are an effective way to get people to stay committed to a behavior.

tiniest pledge, you can start to move the boulder on even the most entrenched behaviors.

Studies are easy to find. A popular case study about parents leaving their cars running while waiting to pick up their kids in school zones reveals the impressive power of pledges. When parents drive to pick up their children from school, most of them don't turn the car off. All these cars create pockets of smog next to the school. One particular school tried to stop the parents' habit of leaving the engine idling by putting up signs that said, *"Please turn off your engine."* The signs didn't work. Parents still left their engines on. The school needed to come up with a better idea. They recruited volunteers to ask each driver as they pulled in to the school if they would make a verbal commitment (a pledge) to turning their engine off while they were waiting. To enhance the parents' commitment to the pledge, volunteers asked parents if they would also place a small sticker that identified them as a "pro clean air" vehicle on their dashboard window. Most of the parents agreed to the pledge and to display the small sticker. The pledge worked, and the duration cars idled at the school pick-up zone decreased by 73 percent.(2)

Another study tested the effect of pledges on recycling behavior. It showed that participants who made a commitment to recycle more increased the number of bottles and cans in their recycling bin by 23 percent.(3) The effect of pledges was tested for riding the bus. The researchers invited a group of participants to make a commitment (a pledge) to ride the bus. The researchers then gave free bus

Face in the creative pledge: this picture isn't a pledge, but it could be! This was a fun marketing idea at an indie craft fair. Imagine making a fun and creative cutout with your pledge written on it that you can send out via social media.

passes to a different group of people. While giving out free bus passes *did* cause an increase in bus riding, the group who made the pledge caught the bus 26 percent more frequently than those receiving the free bus tickets.(4) You can imagine when sustainability managers are designing campaigns to influence whole cities of people, that an improvement like this can be a big deal, with the potential to either gain or lose millions of dollars.

There are a few things you can do to make the pledge's effect even stronger. If a person makes a pledge in private, it still works. But the more public the pledge is, the stronger its effect. Pledges that are publicly photographed or published in the newspaper have a stronger pull and get higher rates of follow-through.(5)

You can get creative with pledges. See the picture of my little daughter and I in the cardboard cutout of the two bees? We got this photo at an indie craft fair from a stall that sold some bee-themed products. A lady who worked at the stall would photograph anyone who put their face in the sign using that person's own phone. Those of us who were photographed were then invited to post our bee picture to Instagram and tag the company so that we could win a prize. It was a fantastic social media marketing idea. At your next event, if this kind of thing suits your audience, you could try making a cut-out of a fun character or animal, like Nemo the clownfish, holding a sign that says *"I pledge to quit using plastic bags."* You could have the creature holding a chalkboard so people could each write their own unique pledge on it. I hope to do something like this one day with a big cut-out of a planet called Sun-Nand-Earth (computer joke). You never know how much a chunk of behavioral science with a dash of creativity really can change the world.

MONEY AS A MOTIVATOR

It's easy to assume that money is the *one big thing* that can motivate just about anyone to do just about anything. I hear people say over and over again, *"We just need to CHARGE people for it!"* meaning that we need to charge money for pollutants we don't want, like garbage and carbon dioxide, so that people make less of it. Be careful of assuming that money is the holy grail of influencing people. The motivational center of the human mind has several different doors we can enter. Money is one door, and it's not *necessarily* the best or the most direct door. In some situations, a financial incentive or penalty might be the magic bullet you need. Other times it doesn't motivate people at all, or weirdly, it can even make people do *more* of the thing you're fining them for.

Charging for disposable shopping bags is an example where a mandatory fee works great. When local governments force supermarkets to charge shoppers 25 cents for each bag, people suddenly start bringing their reusable bags to the store, and overall plastic bag use can plummet by up to 90 percent.(6) Charging people a fee to drive their car through a city center is also a successful way to reduce traffic congestion. Stockholm enforced a congestion charge and it cut the number of cars driving into the city by 25 percent.(7)

In other situations, financial incentives can cause people to do some unexpectedly bad things. Switzerland brought in what's called a "Pay Per Throw" system for garbage collection. Households pay a fee to throw out their garbage depending on how much they produce. It sounds like a good idea at first— charging people for garbage by weight would obviously incentivize people to make less waste, right? In practice, pay-per-throw leads to illegal dumping and people stuffing their excess garbage into overflowing public street trash cans. An approach that uses behavioral drivers such as reporting waste data to households, comparing households against each other, and providing rewards for good performance (like I've been developing with Zerowastify.com) could achieve comparable or better waste reduction, without the negative side effects.

Attaching a financial penalty to a behavior you want to dissuade can even make your mission go backward. Contrary to what you might assume, a price or a fee can even *erode* people's natural motivation to do the right thing. A study conducted on a daycare center revealed this curious phenomenon. Parents were frequently late to collect their children at this particular daycare. You would think that charging parents one dollar per minute for being late would motivate parents to arrive on time. The research team implemented these late fees and monitored what happened. The new fee actually caused the parents to be even later.(8) Why?

Behavioral psychologists explain that we operate with two minds. One mind is *socially* driven, and makes decisions based on what is the "right thing to do." Most of us don't litter. It's not because we're afraid of getting a fine or getting caught by the police. We don't litter because it's within our moral identity and because our community perceives littering as a bad thing. When you start to think about it, most of the good gestures we do, such as helping a neighbor with her groceries, returning a lost wallet, or paying into a small farm's honesty box, are not because of a financial threat or incentive. We do these actions because of our own moral code.

The other kind of mind we have is *financially* driven, and its job is to calculate the best decision for us based on the best economic outcome. This is a good mind to use when you are making important financial decisions such as buying a house or a car. Your financial mind gets you the best deal, but your *social mind* builds your human relationships and moral identity.

When it comes to the daycare study, parents had been trying to collect their kids on time because they had an internal moral drive to do so. Once the

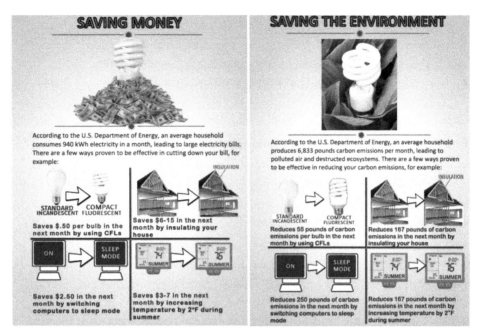

Money or carbon: when these two flyers were tested, it was found that the environmental message resulted in more energy savings among people who vote Democrat.

researchers interjected and put a price on lateness, the parent's thinking moved from the *social* decision-making mind to the *financial* decision-making mind. When parents were paying for the privilege of being late, they felt greater latitude to do so. They were paying for the late minutes, so why not?

What about trying to persuade people to save energy? Do people care more about saving money or preventing carbon dioxide pollution? Most people expect that everyone is motivated to save money, and not carbon dioxide, but we can only know the answer by putting it to the test. A study investigated the effect of these approaches by showing two different flyers to people to see which message affected the participants' energy use.

The first flyer said, *"SAVING THE ENVIRONMENT: An average household produces 6,833 pounds of carbon emissions per month, leading to polluted air and destroyed ecosystems."*

The second flyer said, *"SAVING MONEY: An average household consumes 940 kWh of electricity in a month, leading to large electricity bills."*

Which flyer got a better result? The *SAVING MONEY* flyer worked on everyone who saw it, but it only worked a little bit. The *SAVING THE ENVIRONMENT* flyer worked better than the money flyer, but it only had an effect on half the

Americans in the test group. Can you guess which half it was? Anyone identifying a political orientation as liberal or Democrat was substantially more responsive to a message about carbon dioxide than a message about saving money.(9)

Another study tested two different kinds of messages on the dashboard display of a Toyota Prius. One showed the carbon dioxide released while driving, and the other showed the financial cost of fuel. The research revealed similar results. Drivers saved more fuel when the display showed carbon dioxide savings than when the screen showed financial savings. The study explained a pretty good reason why these financial messages don't work as well as we think they might. It's because the money a person can save on a daily or even monthly basis is pretty small. We're talking 5 cents here, 23 cents there. These small savings on fuel and electricity costs aren't significant enough to motivate people to change. But three kilograms of carbon dioxide? No one really knows what three kilograms of carbon dioxide looks like, but we all know it threatens polar bears, and that's enough to motivate us to change.(10)

There's no silver bullet or black-and-white answer to when and where to use economic pressure to motivate people to change. Financial incentives, fines, and messages about saving money can obviously be effective sometimes, but these measures are not the only tool in our toolkit to change the world. There are often many low-hanging fruit behavioral techniques available that you can use before going for the more heavy-handed approach of using financial pressure. You might be surprised by how much change you can achieve by harnessing people's innate desire to do the right thing, to do better than their neighbors, and to get a smiley face sticker when all their co-workers are watching.

NORMS & IMITATION

We all unconsciously copy the behaviors of others. You do it all the time without realizing it. Imagine that you are getting ready to go to a function. You'll most likely want to dress to fit in with the crowd. Will everyone be dressed in punk, couture, or corporate? It might feel as weird to be the only person in a pressed corporate suit at a punk rock concert as it would to wear an iridescent spiked leather vest to a corporate boardroom lunch—unless perhaps you are Lady Gaga.

Once you are at the party you'll also quickly adopt what the other people are doing. If people are sitting down at tables, you'll also sit down. If they are leaving finished plates in a stack, you'll leave them in the stack, too. If everyone is leaving disposable plates all over the place and making lots of mess, unfortunately, you'll do that, too.(11) You can weave the power of human imitation into your project.

Norms: Opower's TED talk about the various messages tested on people to encourage them to use less energy. The first three messages failed to get a result. The fourth message, "Your neighbors use less," was successful in getting people to reduce energy use.

All you need to do is show people, by example, the things you want them to do, and let them know that lots of other people are doing those things, too.

The company Opower ran a test that showed four different messages to people to see which one worked best to get them to save energy. The messages said *Save money, Save the planet, Be a good citizen,* or *Your neighbors use less than you.* Which message do you think had the best result? The first three had no effect. The fourth message that said *Your neighbors use less than you* worked. It got people to save energy. Why? The human mind is piqued to constantly survey what others are doing, and change one's own actions to fit the norm. That's why this one message got results while the others didn't.(12)

Personal trainers are known for yelling supposedly motivating phrases at you like *"C'mon! You can do it!"* or *"Five more to go!"* to get you to exercise harder. But does it work? A study tested how people responded to their personal trainer in two different scenarios. In the first scenario, the trainer told the person what exercises to do and then tried to motivate subjects by saying motivational phrases to them. In the second scenario, the trainer did neither. The trainer simply led by example and didn't give instruction or use any motivating words. Which group did better? The second group where the trainer simply *led by example.*(13)

Behavioral psychologists call group behaviors *norms.* When someone copies what the group is doing, it's called *normative behavior.* Norms can be categorized in a few different ways. It's important to understand the nuance between each of the different norms because, depending on which one you use, one norm can get people to change, and another norm can actually make your campaign go backward. Choosing your words carefully around the concept of norms for a major campaign can get the change you want to see virally spreading through your community. Choosing the words poorly with the wrong kind of norms could turn the whole campaign into a waste of time and money.

Gregg Sparkman from Stanford University does a good job of describing the various norms in an interview we did on the *How to Save the World* podcast about how to get people to eat less meat.

Static descriptive norm: The statement *"Most people eat meat"* describes a static descriptive norm. The statement is simply telling you what everyone else is doing. It doesn't provide instructions or any moral weight. The classic research on social norms says that the more people do something, the more influential it becomes. If a statement read *"Eighty-nine percent of people eat meat,"* then a person is likely to do what all those other people are doing—to join the majority. If a statement read *"Three percent of people eat a plant-based diet,"* this message infers that it's *not* normal to eat plant-based and this can deter people from adopting the behavior.

Static prescriptive norm: The statement *"Most people think eating meat is a good, healthy, and nutritious thing to do"* is called a static prescriptive norm. This statement conveys the idea of what most people think is the right thing to do. It is not necessarily based on facts, but on the opinion of the majority.

Injunctive norm: The statement *"People should eat more vegetables because it's healthier and better for the environment"* is an example of an injunctive norm. It describes what people *ought* to be doing.

Dynamic descriptive norm: That statement *"Meat consumption the United States has gone down by about 12 percent since 2008"* is a dynamic descriptive norm. It describes the growing or declining *rate of change* over time. Gregg's research found that a dynamic norm message doubled the number of vegetarian meals ordered at a café they studied.(14) Dynamic norms are important because often when trying to affect environmental and social change, telling everyone about the norm likely ends up as a statement that would read, *"Hardly anyone is doing this very important thing."* These statements that focus on a valiant, yet tiny group can unconsciously turn people away. However, describing the *growth* of the small movement inspires people to join in. Focusing on the *growth* and not the *net percentage* is thought to work because most people want to be a part of a growing trend.

Static Norm

"Recent research has shown that 30 percent of Americans make an effort to limit their meat consumption. That means 3 in 10 people eat less meat than they otherwise would."

Dynamic Norm

"Recent research has shown in the last 5 years, 30 percent of Americans have now started to make an effort to limit their meat consumption. That means that in recent years, 3 of 10 people have changed their behavior and began to eat less meat than they otherwise would."

People standing in line at a café who received the dynamic norm message (that revealed a change over time), were twice as likely to order a meatless lunch. The amount of people ordering a vegetarian lunch jumped from 17 percent to 34 percent.

Beware of falling into the trap of telling the world how most people are doing a bad thing. One day at my spiritual home, the California Academy of Sciences, I came across this mistake used in the gift shop. Next to their beautiful display of designer reusable water bottles was a sign that said, *"The average American consumes 160 plastic water bottles every year."* This norm statement might just end up getting people to use *more* plastic because it accidentally normalizes a bad behavior. A better message would read, *"300 people every week quit using disposable plastic bottles. Join the plastic-free revolution,"* or *"Every year 250,000 people buy reusable bottles like this to replace disposable plastic water bottles."* You can easily change the wording on anything you are working on to reflect a positive social trend that people will want to join.

Norms can be displayed with images as well as words. You can illustrate a

Using the wrong end of norms: a sign intended to encourage people to stop buying plastic bottled water may actually encourage people to use more plastic water bottles because they perceive the action displayed as normal.

norm using a photograph of a person *doing* the action you want them to do. Instead of showing a negative norm in the form of a picture of littered plastic bottles, show an image of a rock star happily recycling. Instead of showing animal cruelty, show images of families happily making burgers with faux-meat patties. Instead of showing pictures of plastic in the ocean, show pictures of a lovely woman enjoying her plastic-free lunch. Visually display the trend in a way others can *imitate*.

Have a look through your project's visual and written material and see how you can include positive norm statements and images. You can even test various versions of your statement for the different norm cases. An example sentence might read, *"75 percent of your neighbors compost,"* or *"Most people eat a vegetarian lunch."* You don't have to use a number. You could write, *"People are doing more than ever before."* People want to be a part of what you're doing. People love your cause. Let everyone know that.

STEP #6: BEHAVIOR EXERCISE

1. Actors: Determine who your actors or target audience types are.

2. Actions: For each actor, write down the action, or actions you want him or her to take.

3. De-clustering: De-cluster each action you have identified into the simplest behavior possible until there are no variations on the behavior.

4. Quantify the impact: Where possible, quantify at what scale your target behaviors will affect the data you are trying to change.

5. Choose a sub-behavior: Chose one sub-behavior to focus on. Each sub-behavior will need its own strategy.

6. User/behavior story mapping: Create a user story mapping diagram. Track your user or actor from when she wakes up in the morning, all the way until she engages in the desired behavior and completes the action.

7. Physical environment: How can you alter the environment surrounding the actor to encourage the behavior?

8. Foot-in-the-door: How can you reduce your ask of people to a very small request to which a high number of people might agree?

9. Pledges: How can you bring pledges into your campaign?

10. Norms: Look through the copywriting on your website and promotional material and look at how you are using norms. How can you add normative statements to your campaign?

11. Imitation: How can you model or seed behaviors that people can copy in real life? How can you use images that show an example or a person doing the action? How can you phrase a statement that says, *"Most people are doing the action now"*?

Beware of doing this
Beware of tacking on a "call to action" after you've developed your idea or project. Establish your behavior map first; isolate the action you want people to take; *then* build your project concept up as a means to make people do this action.

STEP #7

SYSTEMS THINKING

"The behavior of a system cannot be known just by knowing the elements of which the system is made."— Donella Meadows, *Thinking in Systems: A Primer*

Are your actions governed by your own unique thoughts and desires, or are they governed by the nature of the *system* in which you exist, such as the rules, other humans, objects, noises, and architecture surrounding you? Did your friend order a beef sandwich at a café last week (even though she wants to start eating less meat) because of the way the sandwiches were arranged in the window, or did she choose beef over tofu *entirely* of her own unique free will?

Systems thinking rejects the assumption that every human always functions independently. It looks at the system as a whole with many people in it, and many forces at work that shape a person's behavior. In particular, it looks at the *interaction* between people, objects, cities, and organizations. Systems theory has many complex nuances and abstractions, but for this chapter, we're going to look at its practical application of getting more humans to do more good things. Through this lens, systems thinking can be consolidated into a general principle that most people's behavior can only be as good as the system in which they exist.

Think of it like this—imagine one day you're out on the road, and you've drunk the last sip of water from your trusted refillable water bottle. You're a motivated environmental citizen, and every day you remember to bring it with you. But now you're thirsty and getting agitated by the heat. Even though you despise plastic bottled water, you end up reluctantly purchasing one at a gas station because there isn't a tap anywhere. The same thing happens next month at an airport. Then again two weeks later at your doctor's office. You buy the disposable plastic bottle not because you *want* to, but because there simply isn't any fresh running water anywhere nearby.

If you're working on a project to get rid of disposable plastic, your campaign needs to be designed in a way that changes *the system* that causes people to rely so heavily on bottled water. An approach that makes people feel bad about using plastic, like making a video, or sending out a "top green tips" flyer alone, won't cut it. In this scenario, *changing the system* means installing more drinking water refill stations.

Targeting the system vs the individual

This distinction between *the individual and the system* is a concept fundamental to the craft of world-changing. If you don't clearly understand the forces at work that are sculpting people's actions, then you and people around you might run the risk of suffering from a bias towards blaming individuals and not hitting the nail on the head of what's causing your problem.

Individual blame bias is all around us. You may have heard sentiments like this before,"*People don't recycle because they are lazy,*" "*The military abuses prisoners because they had 'a few bad apples,'*" "*People drink milk because they are selfish and don't care about cows,*" or "*Kids are doing badly in school because of lousy teachers.*" Each of these statements blames *the individual* instead of the system these people are living in that caused the behaviors.

Imagine a nine-year-old boy who is badly misbehaving at school. Do we blame the child himself, and discipline him accordingly? Or do we look at the larger system in which he is living? He lives in a home that is unloving and often violent. His parents don't read books to him. His older brother is in jail. Is he just a "bad apple," or is he a victim of his environment? If we want to solve his problem

Is it the system's fault? Did the system make everyone do it?

Or are many people individually doing the same bad thing?

behavior, it's easy to see from this example that an individual bias could lead to him getting punished, which would make his already difficult life even worse. He might be provided with a school therapist which, although helpful, won't change the dynamics in his family. We need to look at the larger system in which he exists and change the forces that have shaped his family and shaping him.

Systems thinking might sound like a hip lexicon that designers use in San Francisco, but systems thinking has serious consequences. Ideas that target the individual without looking at the system can be ineffective at best, and socially devastating at worst. Let's look at the mother of all social monstrosities, that occurred *specifically* from the mistake of blaming the individual: American prisons. In the USA, two million people are in jail at any time.(1) The financial cost of incarcerating so many souls is astronomical: $260 billion a year, and thought to exceed $1 trillion when you include the costs to the families, children, and communities of those incarcerated.(2) By comparison, NASA gets about $20 billion in annual funding and the EPA gets $8 billion—that's 8 percent and 3 percent respectively of America's annual prison budget.(3,4)

Perhaps this mountain of funding might be worth it if the system worked. Criminologist William R. Kelly describes it as *"An undeniably poor return on investment"* and claims that well over 65 percent of criminals recommit a crime as soon as they are out.(5) The system has failed because it's built on the premise of punishing *individuals*, and not fixing the *system* that causes crime. This mistake has manifested the collateral damage of devastating millions of people's lives, doing it very expensively, and the darker absurdity of failing at its fundamental reason for existing—to stop people from committing crime in the first place.

The systems-thinking approach to crime looks different. A Canadian study revealed that 100 percent of prisoners—that's *every single person* in Canadian prisons—come from a low-income household that is designated in the poverty category. The systems-

Where do your ideas sit on the *Individual -> Systems* scale?

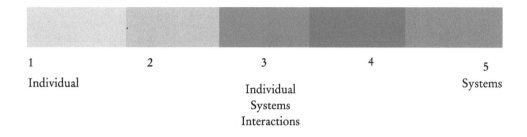

1   2   3   4   5

Individual   Individual   Systems
                     Systems
                     Interactions

1   Individual: I only look at the actions of individual people.

3   Individual + System + Interactions: I look at how the individual actions are influenced by the system, and how to improve the system for improved individual action.

5   System: I only look at systems, policy, infrastructure, government, regulations.

informed message the authors released was, *"We need to get tough on poverty if we want to get tough on crime."*(6)

     The prison example is extreme, but gentler examples of individual bias reducing the effectiveness of social good projects are everywhere. A vegan activist group might succumb to excessive individual bias and focus on trying to get people to stop eating meat and make their vegan status part of their personal moral identity. The activist might try to recruit new followers by offering out a vegan a magazine or sending out tweets. It's not hurting anyone, but it's slow going to get traction in the movement that way. A *systems approach* to reducing meat consumption might involve getting a school or college campus cafeteria to pledge to adopt a low-meat policy. They might agree to serve no more than one-quarter of their food options containing meat and the other three-quarters of their meals to contain only plant-based ingredients, preventing hundreds of meat dishes from being eaten every day, and also quietly promoting the cause by example.

     Think of a campaign to stop the use of plastic shopping bags. Mandatory prices on plastic bags, such as 10 cents to 50 cents per bag at the checkout, have caused disposable bag use to drop by up to 90 percent in many cities. In this case, a regulation focus for your campaign is your best bet for most cities. Asking people to individually use a reusable bag won't come close to having this system-wide impact.

     Don't invest your energy into influencing 1,000 people to each take a separate

Individual vs System

When you are developing your world-changing project, reflect on whether you are trying to influence individuals directly, or you are trying to influence the *system* in which individual people function. You may be able to have a much bigger impact by finding a way to influence the system.

Eat less meat

Individual <<   vs   >> System

- Ask people on social media to go vegan.
- Make a documentary, book or festival asking people to go vegan.

- Get a school to do meat-free Monday.
- Promote a meat-free catering policy for corporations and airlines.
- Improve animal cruelty laws, driving up the price of meat, and reducing demand.

Use less plastic bags

Individual <<   vs   >> System

- Ask people to give up plastic bags through green tips blogs, advertising signs, and YouTube videos.

- Mandatory plastic bag fee of 25c.
- Insert a door hanger bag-remembering sign in new reusable bags
- Give out free door hooks to residents

Kids to eat more vegetables

Individual <<   vs   >> System

- Ask kids to eat more vegetables by putting up signs & sending flyers to parents.

- In school cafeteria, place vegetable dishes close-to-reach, and unhealthy food in hard-to-reach locations.

Stop litter

Individual <<   vs   >> System

- Ask people to pick up litter off the beach.

- Fine companies for litter that has their logo on it.
- Install more bins in high litter areas.
- Add interesting color and shape to bins.

Zero waste menstruation

Individual <<   vs   >> System

- Make YouTube videos asking women to switch to cloth pads and silicone cups.

- Create a partnership with a college, water authority, and a supplier to give out free eco-period kits to young women.

A person's behavior can only be as good as the system in which that person exists.

individual action. Figure out something that no one has ever done before that influences 10,000 people to *react* to the system. Programs that change whole schools, alter the urban infrastructure, re-design the nature of products, or flip the way organizations are funded are where you'll find your most exciting and transformative ideas.

The Default Condition

A *default condition* is the easiest and most efficient, or even *automatic* behavior that people choose in a situation. A common example that illustrates the power of the default condition is organ donation rates across different countries. In Austria, Singapore, and France, organ donation rates are over 95 percent. In the United States, they linger at about 50 percent. Some countries are even as low as 15 percent.(7) Why? It's due to a *default condition* designed into the forms you fill out when you get your driver's license.

Countries with high rates of organ donation use the "opt out" principle in their forms. That means that there's a box you can tick that says something like:

"I hereby object to the removal of organs" or *"Check this box if you do NOT want to be an organ donor."*

Most people don't tick the box, and so they end up as organ donors. The opposite default condition is used on most driver's license forms in the USA.

An "opt in" form might read like this:

"Would you like to be an organ donor?" Then you have to tick a box that says *"Yes."*

Only half the population ticks the box.

FULL NAME (as in NRIC): _____   **DATE OF BIRTH**: _____

NRIC NO.: _____   **SEX**: Male   Female   **RACE**: Chinese   Malay   Indian   Others _____
(please specify)

CITIZENSHIP / RESIDENTIAL STATUS: S'pore Citizen   S'pore Permanent Resident   **TEL NO.**: _____

HOME ADDRESS: _____   **POSTAL CODE**: _____

I hereby object to the removal of the following organ(s) for transplantation upon my death (please tick " ✓ " one or more as applicable):

Saya tidak bersetuju membenarkan organ saya yang berikut didermakan untuk kegunaan pemindahan (transplantation) setelah saya meninggal dunia (tandakan " ✓ " yang perlu):

我反对逝世后，我的下列器官作为移植用途 (请在适当的地方打 "✓" 号):

என் இறப்புக்குப் பிறகு, பின்வரும் உறுப்புகள் மாற்று அறுவை சிகிச்சைக்காக அகற்றப்படுவதற்கு நான் மறுப்பு தெரிவிக்கிறேன் (அணைடுவந்து பொருத்தமான கட்டத்தில் அல்லது கட்டங்களில் இந்தக் குறியை "✓" இடவும்):

Kidney	Liver	Heart	Cornea
Ginjal	Hati	Jantung	Kornea
肾脏	肝脏	心脏	眼角膜
சிறுநீரகங்கள்	கல்லீரல்	இதயம்	வெண்படலம்

Leveraging the default state: A Singaporean "opt out" form for organ donation. If the person filling out the form does nothing (does not tick the box), they are assumed an organ donor.

What does this have to do with systems thinking? It's not that people in some countries *individually* care more about saving people's lives than others. It's simply easier to go with the flow and leave a box on a form empty. The *system* is designed to create the desired behavior. Many undesirable things in the world exist not because there are evil forces at work, but just because the habit to do otherwise has not yet been formed. There are default conditions everywhere that can be switched around and could yield huge results.

Here are some ideas to switch the default state:

Airline food: The default meals provided on an airline could be plant-based. Passengers can make a special request for a meat dish.

Milk: The default milk provided in an office, café, or conference could be almond milk. People can ask for cow's milk as an alternative.

Coffee cups: The default cup offered to customers at coffee shops and food vendors could be a reusable cup. Every customer should be asked, *"Would you like your coffee in a ceramic mug or would you like your own reusable cup for one dollar?"* (Starbucks sells reusable cups for one dollar). The customer would need to circumvent the default cup offerings and ask for a disposable cup.

Retirement funds: The default retirement or superannuation funds you are allocated by your bank or employer should be a responsible investment fund that actively invests in renewable energy and has divested from undesirable industries such as coal and tobacco. An employee would need to make a special request to be transferred away from the ethical fund.

What can you do to affect the system?

Price: Add fees, taxes or fines to the undesired action. Subsidize the cost of the desired action.

Convenience: Position undesired things (such as junk food, cigarettes, or the trash can) in difficult to reach or less-visible places.

Beauty / novelty: Design things to be visually interesting, such as rainbow-colored stairs to encourage people to walk up them.

Rewards: Give a reward like a cheerful sound, sticker, badge, positive statement, creative animation, thanks, score, or free gift.

Corporate policy: Get companies to adopt policies such as company-wide meat-free catering, recycled paper, or electric vehicle fleets.

The law: Persuade the government to make an undesired action a finable offense or make it illegal.

Size: Make desired things larger in size, such as a large opening on a compost bin, and a small opening on a trash can.

Disclosure of data: Make the numbers in the system's feedback loop visible to people and update the numbers regularly.

Infrastructure: Provide safe bike lanes, trees, and bike lockers to encourage exercise and car-free travel.

Default condition: An airline provides a plant-based meal as the default selection unless you specify a meat meal before you fly.

Sound: Create a beeping noise or chime to deter a behavior, such as the beep your car makes when your seatbelt is not on, or the ATM makes when your card is still in the machine.

Women's bathrooms: The default vending machine in women's bathrooms should sell reusable cloth pads and silicone cups. Women seeking disposable products would need to go to a store elsewhere.

Water refill stations: The default drinking water system should be abundant and convenient filtered water refill stations. Plastic bottled water for purchase should always be more difficult to access than a water refill station.

Trash can: The default arrangement of trash cans should position the compost bin closer and with a larger opening than the trash bin.

Healthy eating: The default location of the healthy plant-based foods in a school or workplace cafeteria should be the most visible and easiest to reach. Junk food and animal product food should be somewhat obscured from view.

What opportunities are there in your project to switch the default condition?

Your project as a system

Does your system have all the components to make a systemic virtuous upward spiral of change?

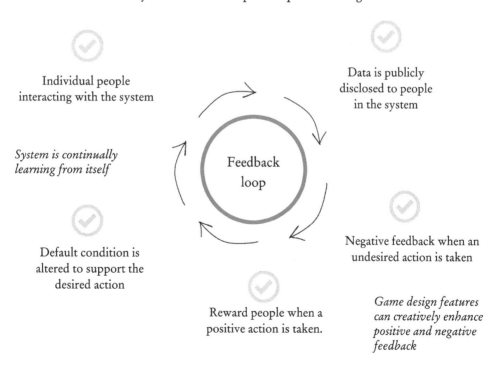

Individual people interacting with the system

System is continually learning from itself

Default condition is altered to support the desired action

Feedback loop

Data is publicly disclosed to people in the system

Negative feedback when an undesired action is taken

Game design features can creatively enhance positive and negative feedback

Reward people when a positive action is taken.

The Feedback Loop, Learning, & Causality

The feedback loop is a fundamental concept in systems thinking. We go into the feedback loop more later, but for the context of this chapter, let's look at one special feature of a feedback loop—its ability to learn from itself over time. Think of your whole project as if it is an organism that is constantly gathering data and learning from what it collects, and how it continually uses this data to grow and evolve. A system with a feedback loop is always *learning* and *optimizing*.

If your project isn't built around a feedback loop of data, the project itself won't be able to learn what initiatives your team undertakes that affect the data, and what they do that doesn't work to change anything. You could end up in an infinite loop of doing the same thing year in and year out, such as holding the same conference, selling the same product, or publishing to the same blog, and not affecting the cause you are trying to change.

The closer you get to your feedback loop of data, the better you'll be able to identify the *causal mechanism* for what makes change happen in your project. A system changes because of some *causality*: the thing that *causes* the change to happen. That might sound obvious, but you'd be amazed how often we get our theories of causality scrambled. Think of how often you've heard people say this, *"It's greed. It's capitalism. It's selfishness. It's political donations. It's education. It's consumerism. It's lack of awareness. It's corruption. It's the patriarchy. It's quarterly stock market returns. It's rich people. It's poor people. It's God."* Even experts often struggle to identify the exact drivers of human behavior. If there's one thing to take from this book, it's a ruthless devotion to discovering your project's causality—and your feedback loop is your partner in discovering it.

Measurement, the disclosure of data, the feedback loop, and the agency (motivation) that numbers provide people all fit together to make the architecture of a system that is able to learn and grow in a positive, self-improving upward spiral of change. The theories of interconnected feedback, causality, and self-learning are big concepts to understand. A feedback loop gives you the chance to *reward* people when they do something good, and people love rewards. The next chapter on game design explores how to apply your creativity to augment your system with designs that captivate, reward, motivate and ultimately make the whole game of change *fun*.

STEP #7: SYSTEMS THINKING

1. Individual bias: Check if your ideas are leaning too heavily on trying to encourage individuals to take action, without looking to the surrounding environment. Your ideas can be more effective when you change *the system* that affects individual behavior.

2. Physical environment: Map out the physical environment people are moving through and see how you can make changes to buildings, infrastructure, and supply chains.

3. Default selection: See if there are any undesirable default selections embedded in the system that you can flip to a more desirable default selection.

4. Legislation that shifts the data: Investigate what kind of policies or legislation would be effective in shifting the numbers on your cause. Investigate what policies you can bring into your local city to help your cause. Another city may have brought in a successful policy you can emulate. Learn how your local city's advocacy process works and how you can get involved. Government is designed to be influenced by its constituents.

5. Organization policy: What policies can you bring into organizations such as a school, company, or department you might be involved in that can affect the whole group?

6. Causality and the feedback loop: Study in detail the causality of what drives change in your project or idea. Make sure your feedback loop informs your assumptions on causality so your project is always pushing a correct assumption.

7. Continual improvement: Build a feedback loop that monitors and encourages continual improvement in your system.

STEP #8A

GAME DESIGN

"90 percent of what is considered impossible is, in fact, possible. The other 10 percent will become possible with the passage of time and technology." – Hideo Kojima, game designer

Could saving the world be a game? Hell yeah, it can. But you have to do it right. Using game design to change the world isn't about making yet another addictive iPhone game. We're not here to make *"Angry Birds for Recycling."* We can do better than that. When we interweave game design principles with the techniques we've been learning about for *how to save the world,* the effect of these techniques coming together can be magical.

Jane McGonigal, author of *Reality is Broken,* is the foremost cheerleader for the cause of making it, in her own words, *"as easy to save the world in real life as it is to save the world in online games."* She talks about how games get us to experience some pretty remarkable sensations: a profound sense of urgency, intense concentration, and deep focus when tackling a difficult problem. Games can lead us to experience blissful productivity and to do it with a feeling of optimism when an epic win is just around the corner. She tells the story of how gamers love to be invested in awe-inspiring missions with planetary-scale meaning. All these components sound like they add up to a darn good skill set for changing the *real* world. McGonigal believes that many of us become the best version of ourselves when we play in *game worlds*: we're optimistic, collaborative, and motivated.

She illustrates a chasm between the delightful world of *games*, and the *real world* of grisly, boring, or uncomfortable tasks. In contrast to game worlds, in real life, we can feel overwhelmed, anxious, depressed, frustrated, and cynical. Does that sound familiar? You've probably had at least a few days like that where it seems like no one is going to do anything about how much plastic is in the ocean, and the world feels like it is, as David Suzuki put it, *"In a giant car heading towards a brick wall and everyone is arguing over where they're going to sit."* Changing the world is hard, and can definitely be imbued with negative feelings. But here's the thing: McGonigal hones in on the interesting insight that we *never* have those feelings when we're absorbed in playing games.

Our job when designing solutions to save the world is to cross this chasm and weave the positive experience of the *game world* together with the *real world actions* it takes to save the world.

Blending *game design* with the art of *saving the world* is quite a different practice than conventional game design. Conventional games are designed purely to be fun and even to be addictive. How much of your childhood was immersed in a mind-meld with *Super Mario* and *Tetris?* Regular games don't need to achieve anything other than the engagement of the player. You enter the game, you play, the game ends, then you leave the game, and go back to regular life. The "fun" that games manifest is trapped within the confines of the game experience and doesn't bleed out into day-to-day actions in regular life, like for example, what kind of coffee cup you choose. When it comes to the separation between the *game world* and the *real world*, change-the-world-games require the opposite approach: your game needs to be generated from, and *embedded in*, actions that take place in the everyday world.

The basis of a game that makes change must be built from two things: 1) a *feedback loop* of the *real world data* you are trying to change, and 2) the specific *behavior* you are trying to influence. Change-the-world-games are successful only if they can accelerate the *measurable change* your project is making on the *real world numbers* you are trying to affect. The difference between this and regular game design is huge, and when it comes to your design, it changes everything.

The secret to getting the art of game design to work for your cause is that it needs to be built upon a firm foundation of real-world numbers like kilowatt hours or trees, not arbitrary points or scores. Think of game design (or gamification) when applied to social change as *the disclosure of data* that is designed to be fun. The best way to understand how to apply game design to real-world change is to think of it as a kind of *motivational wrapping* that layers around your data and your behavior design.

Data enables a myriad of proven motivational tools like leaderboards, progress bars, positive feedback, rewards (like cute digital strawberries and smiley faces), and social comparisons, that *just aren't available* to you if you don't have measurement at the core of your strategy.

Let's get real about what changing the world *really* involves, and where a game-for-change meets its judgment day. "Saving the world" sounds exciting, and it always looks pretty fabulous when super-heroes do it in the movies. But in practice, saving the world is usually an under-appreciated and unglamorous task. Once you've graduated past the evocative taglines that got you inspired to join the cause in the first place, eventually you realize that *real change* (not just buzz-world-filled events, activist-rap, or art projects that talk about change) is made up of many small, nitty-gritty, and often mundane actions.

The actions it takes to change the world are pedestrian things like getting people to put a banana peel into a compost basket instead of a regular garbage can. It might be getting an office of corporate lawyers to give up their free plastic water bottles. Maybe you need to persuade five different apathetic commercial building managers to take on the inconvenient task of refitting all their buildings with LED lights. Then there are all the actions that people don't like to talk about, like getting women to quit using tampons and adopt the silicone "moon" or "diva" cups or just getting people to flush the toilet less often to save water. You could be trying to get people to use condoms to stop the spread of HIV. Many of the actions it takes to change the world are unglamorous, boring, or even gross.

Just as an elegant piece of software is beautiful to use, while a single line of its code may be simplistic, the discrete actions required to change the world are not very exciting or awe-inspiring when broken down into their components. The movement is exhilarating, yet each little step is a humble act.

How do we take the unglamorous, inconvenient, sometimes expensive, and even confronting behavior-changes we want people to make, and re-imagine them into *fun experiences*, and even make them as addictive as a game? A world-changing superhero shouldn't be scared of getting dirty. The opportunity lies before us to re-design a billion little unglamorous actions into an epic game revolution that can save the world.

GAME DESIGN PRINCIPLES

Learning and mastery: People love to learn, and they love to get good at things. Think of how difficult plastic-free living is. It requires many daily and even hourly lifestyle changes. Chess is difficult, too, yet people love it and it has endured for centuries. A difficult-to-adopt behavior can be turned into a journey of self-mastery.

Novelty: Humans crave novelty. Everything you make needs to be *interesting*. It needs to be *not*-boring. It needs to be *novel*. You can play with color, sound, storytelling, physical space, animation, and whatever you can dream up to make something different and fun that people haven't seen before.

Emotion: We are emotional creatures. Emotions drive most of our behaviors. Think through how you can use faces, animals, and words to invoke a range of emotions in your player, and how you can use these emotions to bond your player to your cause.

Rewards: People get excited about continuing their journey in a game because they are rewarded along the way. It's easy to assume that people need a tangible reward like money or a free vegan hamburger to stay motivated, but purely digital rewards can be similarly or even more motivating. Rewards can take the form of fun animations, badges, points, signs of progress, a new color, or an elevation in rank against other players.

Progress towards a goal: Your player's journey can be structured with a specific beginning and end, as well as all the steps in between. People like to feel they are making progress, and it's easy to visually reinforce it as they go using levels, steps, and creative interpretations of progress bars.

Design an experience: Try to think more broadly than only using a game to catalyze a behavior. Think about designing *a human experience*. Humans are powerfully motivated to pursue new, novel, and interesting experiences. How do you want your player to *feel* when she behaves in a particular way?

Games everywhere: There is more to life than the smartphone. There is infinite real estate you can work with when you start to think outside the screen of personal phones and laptops. Look at the environment around the player and utilize it: walls, billboards, door knobs, parking spaces, community notice-boards,

There's a scene I love in the HBO show *Silicon Valley*. Richard, the show's main character and deep-nerd-hacker, is setting up a table at a large tech expo, when he awkwardly bumps into his ex-girlfriend, Winnie. She's working at an elaborate booth located directly across from his, called *Peace Fare: Make Change Not War*. To make things worse, the flashy stand is owned by Winnie's *new* love interest. She invites "new guy" over. He's tall, athletic, and German. Richard says, "Nice stand," excusing his somewhat pitiful table, "We . . . err . . . thought we'd be more frugal." New guy declares in an emphatic humblebrag with the kind of emphasis better saved for the TED stage, "*We really zink our company's message is worth getting out zhere. When I sold my last company, I realized I had the luxury to invest in something I really believe in: helping humanity thrive. That's why I decided to bring Peace Fare into the world.*"

A few scenes later we see Richard on his laptop. Filled with that specific kind of hateful focus that comes *only* when googling your ex's new lover, Richard is reading up on *Peace Fare*, and stewing. "Is something wrong?" his co-founder Gilfoyle asks in trademark deadpan. "Yes. Very wrong." Richard fidgetly replies. "Peace Fare is a *game*. Look at his website . . . *give virtual coins to virtual homeless people. Grow virtual corn to feed virtual starving villages.* What the *fuck*, right? I mean, he's over there making all this noise about *turning your mobile device into an empathy machine,* but it's not doing *anything*. WE are doing something real. HE is not. What about the idea of growing REAL corn to feed REAL starving people?!"

Moral of the story: *Don't be Peace Fare guy.* Don't make something flash that creates no real change.

From the HBO show Silicon Valley, Season 4 Episode 9: A game called Peace Fare

taps, light switches, tables at cafés, shapes on a floor, towel hangers, outdoor sculptures. Whatever you see around you digital or non-digital—all are on offer as canvases on which to build a game experience.

Design for happiness: Practicing game design and gamification is the art of designing human happiness into action. Games are wired to produce pleasure, and so their design is inseparable from the study of the human mind. How can you design happiness and pleasure into the real-world behaviors you want people to do?

It's easy to forget sometimes that changing the world is all about changing *humans*. Your design needs to be entirely, and deeply, focused on the *human* experience. John Carmack, creator of the famous 90s game *DOOM* said, "*The game designer shouldn't be making a world in which the player is just a small part. The player is the boss: it's your duty to entertain him or her.*" Your job or even your *duty* is to strive to make your players feel, whilst performing the actions in your game experience, that they are playing *the greatest game on Earth*.

The secret behind good game design is that it taps into the *motivational core* of our being. Saving the world does not need to be boring, ever. It can be and *should be* an adventure into creatively applying *the art of fun* to your cause. There are many game mechanics that will brighten your project and send a spark through the hearts and minds of your users. Since I started adding game design techniques to my projects, several people have messaged me about the emotional overwhelm, delight, and even tears, they have experienced when exploring things I've made— which surprised me because the stuff I've made so far is pretty simple. It's been fascinating to see just how getting a few things right, even on a small project, is like a cupid's arrow to the heart.

Many of the design techniques in this chapter are low-hanging fruit that you will be able to easily implement. You can go high-tech and get busy building environmental sensors and smartphone apps. Or you go low-tech and can put a piece of paper on the wall with a measure of plastic bottles used that day in your office, and draw a smiley or frowny face on it. Either with a $2.00 roll of cute cherry stickers or an Arduino micro-controller, there's no limit to what you can do when you put your creativity together with some good numbers.

Don't be afraid to throw down your most colorful and weird ideas. You have permission to create something fabulous. The difference between a dull campaign that struggles to get traction, and one that is explosively captivating, often isn't a whole lot of extra funding, government support, or celebrity endorsements—it's *creativity*. There is no ceiling or cost to the creativity and ideas you can generate in making a project that captivates people and makes them fall in love with what you do. Imagination is free. Making *fun* is a state of mind that you can learn to generate. Apply the techniques in this chapter and see how far you can go in creating the magic of *delight*. We are at the very beginning of what is possible to make changing the world the delightfully fun, imaginative, and colorful experience it should be.

THE FEEDBACK LOOP

How do your members, users, students, teams, or players *know* what impact they are having once they start taking the actions you are prompting them to take? And how do *you know*, with real numbers that you can see, how much change your project is making? It can be a tricky question to answer for many social and environmental change projects, but it's often quite easy to answer for many things with which we are already familiar.

If you are exercising, you might wear a Fitbit device that tells you how many calories you burned during your workout. When you are driving, you can see on the dashboard how fast you are going. Even without using an electronic device, *your body itself* has a biological thermostat inside you that tells you when you are getting too hot or too cold.

These signals help you to respond with an *action*. You can take action by ramping up your workouts to reach your Fitbit goal. You can take action by slowing your car down to stay within the speed limit. You can take action by splashing water on your skin and sitting under a tree to cool off. The system sends you data, and you react by *doing something*. It's a two-way communication system called a *feedback loop,* and it is one of the most important concepts to use in your mission to save the world.

Think of a regular bathroom tap that has *no* feedback loop built in. It doesn't tell you anything about how much water you are using when you turn it on. You are not altering your behavior and adjusting your water usage in response to what the tap might be telling you. There is no communication between *you* and *it*.

Now let's think of a bathroom tap *with* a feedback loop. The tap would be fitted with a gauge that measured how much water the tap uses. It would have a small screen positioned above it, so that every time you used the tap, the screen would tell you, in real-time numbers, how much water you were using. This tap example was prototyped by *The Teague* design agency by attaching an iPad to a tap that displayed the tap's water use. The designers claim that it dropped by a dramatic *75 percent* after adding the feedback loop.(1) That's a huge number. Feedback loops have enormous potential to catalyze change, especially when it comes to anything that is easy to measure.

TRY AGAIN

Motivated from seeing the impact
of their action (or realizing their
last attempt failed) the person
sees the updated data and tries
again to influence the number
with an action.

The Feed

The skeleton of your world-
changing project needs to be built
around a feedback loop of the data
you are trying to change.

REWARD

The person who made the change is
rewarded. The reward could be a
friendly word, a smiley face, a fun
animation, a color change, a sticker, or
a higher placement on a leaderboard.

DATA

Measure the data you are
trying to change.

ACTION

Use the data to push people to
take the action you've identified.

back Loop

Everyone needs to be able to see the
numbers, take an action to shift the
numbers, then see that their efforts
created a change in the numbers.

CHANGE
THE DATA

People do the action. The system
measures this change and stores
the updated information, as
swiftly as possible, and in a way
that everyone can see.

Tap feedback loop: The Teague design agency created a feedback loop for a tap using a water meter, an Arduino, and an iPad. The iPad displayed the amount of water the tap was using. This set-up quickly caused water use to drop by 75 percent.(1)

The Structure of a Feedback Loop

Data: An electronic device or sensor gathers data about the thing you are trying to change, and sends it to a database. Data can also be collected manually, or by surveying people. Data collection should happen in real time if possible.

Action: The data needs to be displayed or communicated to the player *at the point in time* when they are able to take an action. The data is designed to best encourage the desired *action*.

Change the data: Your player takes action, which in turn influences the data. The system records this change and displays the change to the player.

Reward: The player is rewarded for making the change. The player receives positive feedback such as a "good job!" message, a color, points, icons, animations, badges, or an improved rank compared to other players.

Try again: The updated data is communicated to the player, and the player responds in turn with another action. The feedback loop starts again.

A key feature of a well-functioning feedback loop is *timing*. A good feedback loop shows the data it collects immediately, as it's happening, in real time. The speedometer in your car, or the biological temperature sensors on your skin, let you know instantly what is going on. Not all feedback loops get the information back to us so quickly. Some feedback loops are very slow and involve manual labor to gather and publish the data. This is the difficult reality of many data systems used in environmental sustainability and social change projects. Data might only be collected once a year, it might be hard to find, or not even collected at all. One project I worked on involved displaying municipal solid waste (that's regular curbside garbage) data on the internet. I did some research and found that the data, measured in the weight of garbage, wasn't updated instantly when the truck picked up the garbage bin at the curb like I was hoping it would be. It wasn't even updated when the truck got to the landfill. The EPA updated the data *once every two years.* The amount of trash wasn't measured by electronic sensors that put the data into a database that I, or any other software developer, could query. It was collected by human researchers who surveyed the landfills *by hand* and published the data in a PDF report you can download from the EPA website.

The EPA report is interesting, but that feedback loop has a delay of over *two years!* That means anyone working in a waste reduction job, or simply trying to be a good citizen and make less trash, has absolutely no way to know how successful or unsuccessful their efforts have been. Can you imagine if it took *two years* for your Fitbit let you know how many steps you just took? Long latency feedback loops are not fun. We could argue that they are even the enemy of fun.

So, what do feedback loops have to do with games? The blueprint of any game created with the intention of changing the world needs to be made out of a *feedback loop of real-world data.* Game design is a process of *augmenting* your feedback loop to make it even *better* at influencing people. Your game is largely a creative interpretation of the *reward feature* in the feedback loop. Turn five

Can you build a Fitbit for the planet? The Fitbit is an excellent metaphor for what we need for environmental data: to see it quantitatively in real time, so we can be accountable, motivated, and take action.

kilograms, three liters, or 20 kilowatt hours changed up or down in the *real world*, into game rewards for the player, such as +1s, points, badges, progress bars, strawberries, cute animated animals, smiley faces, or whatever your creativity leads you to design. This secret has the power to get you to make something awesome and truly world-changing. The possibilities for building better feedback loops of data, displaying this data to people, and wrapping the whole thing in a fun game-experience, are endless.

The feedback loop does the heavy lifting in influencing human motivation. Examples and studies aren't hard to find. A meta-review of 38 studies involving energy conservation displays showed that feedback about energy use reduced home energy consumption by ten percent. Ten percent is a *big* change when we're trying to reduce energy across millions of homes.(2) In another study, a sign that displayed the quantities of recycled paper was displayed above recycling bins in a university. Upon implementing the sign, the quantity of paper recycled jumped by 77 percent.(3) A similar experiment on aluminum can recycling behavior had the same effect. A sign placed above recycling bins providing feedback about the number of cans recycled during the previous week increased recycling rates by 65 percent.(4) It also works for speeding. The electronic displays you see near school zones that let you know how fast you are going successfully reduce driver speeds by an average of 14 percent.(5) The numbers in these examples are substantial, and they all resulted from the simple addition of a feedback loop.

Whatever it is that you work on, figure out a way to measure it accurately, and send the data to a computer instantly. If the data is already being collected, figure out how to display it to your players. It might be a little bit difficult to do, but it's probably not *that* difficult—nothing a couple of devoted engineers can't figure out in a month or two.

When I was working on the waste project, it was easy to see that we needed load sensors (weighing scales) attached to the garbage truck arm that picks up each load of garbage. Then we'd have the data, and we would be able to do something like send a text message to a household immediately, as the garbage was picked up that said *"Your garbage today was 7.8 pounds, that's down 12% from last week. Great job!"* I found a company that made the scales, and it wasn't too difficult to build an API that interfaced with the truck system and put the data on the internet, in real time. Feedback loop complete.

Leaving the feedback loop out of your mission to change the world is one of the biggest blind spots I see in far too many projects. If you don't design your project on the basis of a feedback loop of real-world data, then it's likely that your project will end up like a broken paddle boat—you'll be paddling hard, but not moving your cause forward. Remember Peace Fare guy from the HBO show "Silicon Valley"? Leaving your project disconnected from a feedback loop of real-world data will make you like Peace Fare guy. Peace Fare guy is stuck in the middle of the lake, going nowhere, and yet, he still thinks he's really cool. Don't be like *Peace Fare guy*.

All over the world there are feedback loops calling out to be created. Building out the feedback loop revolution is a whole new realm of creative technology to explore, where we can design feedback loops to be fun and to entice people to take the desired behavior that will change the world.

AGENCY

Agency is an important word in game design. It refers to the *motivation* or *empowerment* that a player feels. It means *the ability to influence* the world and to specifically influence the player's progress in the game.

The concept of agency in game design has an interesting corollary to environmentally friendly behaviors. People are motivated to do things like compost, or avoid using disposable coffee cups, when they believe that *their actions make a difference*. As it turns out, people with a high sense of personal agency over eco-friendly outcomes are in fact, *more likely* to engage in eco-friendly behaviors than people who merely express that they *care* about environmental issues.(6) *That's crazy*. It means that when it comes to being a good environmental citizen, *agency* is more important than how much you actually *care* about the planet. It also shows that you don't need to work that hard at getting people to care more. However, you *do* need to get them to feel that their actions are making a difference. You need to instill *agency*.

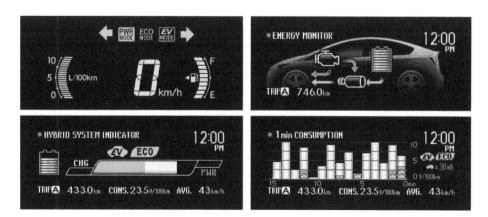

Dashboard display of a Toyota Prius: A real-time feedback loop of the relationship between driver activity and the energy the engine is using. This feedback loop enables the driver to have a sense of agency (empowered motivation) over his or her vehicle's fuel consumption.

Agency and *feedback loops* are partners on the same team. Feedback loops facilitate personal agency by helping people know they are making a difference. This quote about the Toyota Prius dashboard in the *Wired* magazine explains it well, "*Think about how hybrid car owners become obsessed with the dashboard display showing an on-the-fly calculation of gas mileage. The result? They change the way they drive to maximize mileage. It becomes a game and enjoyable challenge complete with quantifiable personal bests.*" Motivation and feedback are two sides of the same coin.

Tightening the latency, or time-lag, of your feedback loop is critical to your potential to maximize agency. The Toyota Prius dashboard's feedback is *immediate*. The player is right there, literally in the driver's seat, able and ready to take action in the moment. The player can see the results of his or her driving behavior without delay. Social media notifications are instant, too. Think of how addictive the red dots are. We know they happen instantly, so it's very easy for us to check, and check again, and keep posting so that we can keep checking it again, and again. It's the *immediacy* of the feedback that compels us to keep going back for more.

Your job as a world-changer is to close the latency gap in your feedback loop as much as you can. The art of making a game that will help save the world will rely heavily upon how fast you can make *that feeling of making a difference* come true, and make it keep happening over and over.

ENVIRONMENTAL DATA LITERACY

You probably know how much you weigh, how much money you have in your bank account, and you might even know how many calories are in an apple. We know plenty of numbers about important things in our lives.

Other numbers are important, too. Do you know how many liters of water you used yesterday? What about how many gallons of gasoline your car used this week? Or how many ounces of plastic you threw into a landfill last year? It's okay if you don't know the answers—nobody does. Currently, our environmental impact, in numbers, is completely invisible to us. Even if you *want* to go out on a limb and work these numbers out, it's still not that easy to do. We are currently experiencing a crisis of *environmental data literacy,* and the lack of available data that reveals our environmental footprint, in numbers, I believe is stifling our ability to make substantial progress in changing the world. If you're curious, here's a glimpse at the environmental footprint of a year in the life of an average American:

- *Burns 3.22 tons of coal each year in coal-power stations.(7)*
- *Consumes 22.2 barrels of oil to power vehicles, heating, and manufacturing.(8)*
- *Uses 6 trees to make paper. (9)*
- *Releases 22.1 tons of carbon dioxide into the atmosphere.(10)*
- *Uses 272 grams of pesticides used to spray crops (a few grams is enough to kill an adult human). (11)*
- *Contributes 810 kilograms (nearly 1 ton) of garbage into landfill. (12)*

The problem isn't just about how unfamiliar we are with these numbers. It goes deeper. The way the data is collected for most environmental indicators, as it stands now, is pretty crude. The numbers listed above are all *averages*. They are one big number for the whole United States, divided by 320 million people. It's almost impossible to get individual environmental data for a single household, a street, or an individual person. This lack of granularity is robbing us of the potential to utilize tremendously powerful principles such as showing people how they rank against each other, assigning a color grade (like we do for fire risk), or giving people positive feedback when they do a good job.

While there are huge holes in our environmental data literacy, it also means there is an epic opportunity to accelerate the revolution of environmental data. The

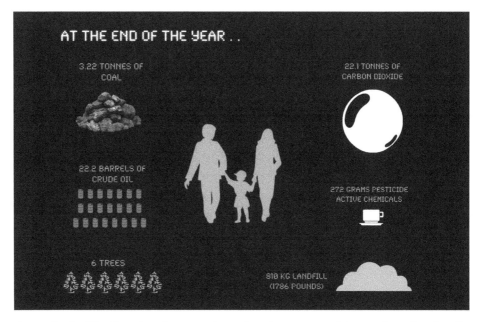

A year in the life of an American: people are largely unaware of the numbers that describe their environmental footprint.

The 350.org campaign: communities around the world creatively displayed the numbers 350 to raise data literacy of what the safe amount of carbon in the atmosphere should be.

world is our oyster when it comes to finding better ways to collect, distribute, and style this data to drive change. You can use smart meters, automatic SMS messaging, low-cost sensors, app notifications, small Raspberry Pi touch screens, big electronic billboards, ticker screens, remote wifi devices, Facebook apps, chrome extensions, Apple watches, Google maps, elevator display screens, satellite images, Arduinos, multi-color LEDs, and a whole bunch of ready-made software tools to build almost any kind of feedback loop you might imagine. You don't need to wait for NASA or Google to do it for you. You can build this stuff in your bedroom.

A recent environmental literacy campaign by climate-focused not-for-profit *350.org* put a challenge out to community groups to take big creative photographs of the numbers *350*. Groups all over the world stepped up and carefully created the 350 shape from umbrellas, flowers, people, seaweed—you name it. The number *350* refers to the amount of carbon dioxide in parts-per-million we can safely have in the atmosphere before heading towards catastrophic climate change. If you're also wondering if we've passed this limit, the Earth's climate passed 400 parts per million (global average atmospheric carbon dioxide) in 2015.(13) The photographs were so novel, interesting, and memorable, you can't help but have that number—350—forever etched into your mind.

You can do it, too. Take steps to make people aware of what the safe or ideal number should be in relation to your cause, and let everyone know what numbers represent critical or dangerous levels. Whether it's the kilowatt hours of electricity consumed in a commercial building, what a basic living wage should be, or the parts-per-million of smog, you can spread these meaningful quantitative messages to your audience in memorable ways. If we work at it, one day, such environmental data literacy will become commonplace. Imagine a world where we'd know the numbers that make up our individual environmental footprint just as easily as we'd know how much food was in our refrigerator, or we could see how much carbon dioxide it took to make a packet of potato chips, just as we read how many calories it contains. We're just beginning to develop the power to wield the numbers around us to manifest a new wave of human action. Data literacy is a whole new paradigm in design and education, and you have the power to push it forward.

COMPARISON

Do you know what one of the most common and predictable human behaviors is? It's our herd behavior. We frequently act in a way that mirrors the people around us. We want to be in the herd, but we also want to be *better* than other herd members. We can leverage the power of social comparison to help motivate people to do more good things. Comparing people or things to each other based on an objective measurable data point is one of the most powerful tools in your social-change toolkit. You can also compare cities, businesses, corporations, teams, campuses, streets, neighborhoods, schools, or just about anything you can measure. There are many creative ways you can display a comparison. You can create simple infographics that compare one player to another player, you can use the first-second-third podium design that is used in athletic events, or you can just use a simple bar chart.

Electricity reporting company *Opower* effectively uses comparison to drive energy efficiency. Opower adds a simple chart to electricity bills that compares a resident's electricity use against their neighbors. It works. These charts achieve an average of three percent reduction in electricity usage.(14) You might think that three percent is not all that high, but considering how simple the intervention is, three percent is a great win just by adding a chart to a bill. To put it in context, air travel also accounts for about three percent of the USA's carbon emissions, so Opower's comparison chart makes as substantial a change as getting a whole city to give up flying.(15). Another company, called Watersmart, uses a similar strategy to that of Opower, sending reports that compare a household's water use to that of its neighbors. The Watersmart reports achieve a five percent reduction in water use on average and help residents discover hidden water leaks that are responsible for about half of all residential water use.(16)

Comparison works for individuals, but can it work for a whole city? A fascinating example that reveals the power of comparison at a civic scale is called *Oklahoma City Goes on a Diet*. It all started one day in 2004 when *Men's Health Magazine* ranked Oklahoma City as *"America's Fattest City."* Oklahoma's mayor was so upset by learning of his city's poor rank and having it disclosed so publicly that he took it to heart, got serious, and went on a mission to change it. He launched a campaign called "One Million Pounds" and challenged his city, which included himself, to lose a collective one million pounds.(17)

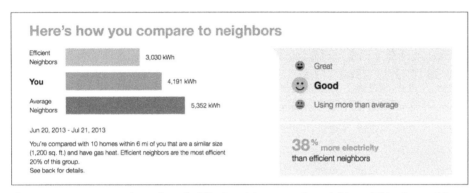

Opower report: comparing a household's electricity use to its neighbors. This chart achieves an average of three percent reduction in energy usage.

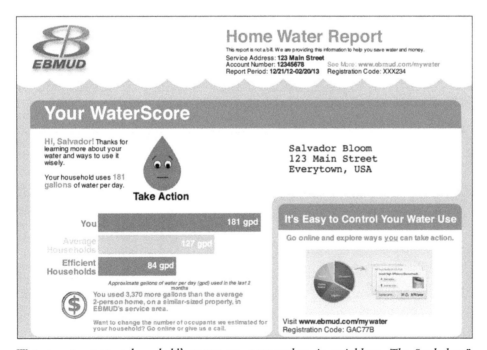

Watersmart report: a household's water use compared to its neighbors. The "red drop" character is used to push high water-use households to take action.

Use a graphic to compare how much water one person uses versus another.

Compare the impact of different products with a number and shape showing the scale.

Present your players in terms of their rank in first, second, or third place.

Compare different pesticide use on types of apples, indicated by size and color.

The campaign was a remarkable success. More than 47,000 citizens tracked their weight and logged their lost pounds on the campaign's website. Five years later, the city's residents reached their goal of collectively losing one million pounds. The city also passed a one percent tax to fund urban greening, bike paths, and health programs, which apparently was passed through local government without contest.

This is a fun case study in itself, but what is particularly interesting is that what motivated the change was being *ranked*. Everybody knows they need to exercise and to eat vegetables, but just because we *know* what we *should do* doesn't mean we do it. What does it take to turn *knowing* what we *should* be doing into motivation so strong it builds a movement of tens of thousands of people and lasts for years? It was the force of taking the actual numbers, putting them in order, and publicly disclosing them. No one *wants* to be overweight, but people *especially* don't want to be known as residents of America's Fattest City. Numbers, when used used in ranking, can inspire miracles.

What can we compare?

Granular data can be powerful because it allows us to compare all kinds of people, things, and places to each other. This matters because people become wildly motivated when their performance is compared to the performance of someone or something else. Design your data to compare people, groups, and things in way that is going to motivate them to make a change. Here are some ideas:

City to
City

School to
School

Person to
Person

Building to
Building

Corporation to
Corporation

University to
University

House to
House

Block to
Block

Suburb to
Suburb

Forest to
Forest

Government to
Government

Building Material to
Building Material

Lake Shore to
Lake Shore

Food to
Food

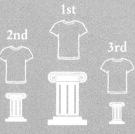

Product to
Product

Factory to
Factory

Café to
Café

Storm Water
Drain to Storm
Water Drain

LEADERBOARDS

A leaderboard is a public display of people or groups, ranked in order of position. Leaderboards exist entirely to leverage the power of social comparison, and they can have a profound impact. One study found that students who were given leaderboards that ranked the students' scores interacted with their project an average of *thirty times* more often than students who weren't ranked on a leaderboard.(18) A multiple of thirty times is a dramatic improvement, and you can use leaderboards to improve the outcomes of your project, too.

Why does rank have such a powerful affect on us? Humans are not solitary, self-reliant animals like octopuses, cats, or sharks. Humans are, at our core, social beings, and are actually the most socially interconnected species on the planet. Each one of us relies on a vast and complex social web to provide us with food, water, safety, and all the things we need to survive.

It's not just about material survival, though. Social connections are the currency of human happiness. Our human relationships are so fundamental to us, that the *one* factor that most highly correlates with life expectancy isn't diet, exercise, or even smoking, which you might assume—it's the frequency and depth of our human relationships.(19) The richness of our friendships, respect from our peers, and feeling valued by others are made from a fabric of carefully nuanced interactions. The one thing that spans across all people, from all cultures, is that we all experience our greatest grief at the loss of, or separation from, a loved one. We'll do just about anything to stop it from happening.

Our social nature means we are quick to evaluate our position in respect to people around us. Being the worst in the pack is an undesirable place to be. Being the best in the pack, or at least better than average, can unleash the great riches of being liked, respected, valued, desired, or even admired. This is why leaderboards and social comparison work so well—they speak to the core of our inner social animal. You can see how it's quite a different door to the human mind than telling people *facts* about your cause.

Sometimes people wonder if leaderboards might have a negative effect on groups, such as encouraging a jealous rivalry that could repress the spirit of open collaboration. A leaderboard is really about designing for the *accountability* and *transparency* of your data. Research on leaderboards shows that it's not entirely the spirit of *competition* that drives change.(18) The numbers on a leaderboard provide a motivational flag that spurs a person or a team to start problem-solving to improve their score. Although the leaderboard ranks players individually, it can spur all the players to work together to solve the problem. I see this kind of gamification design as a fuel that turns our *intrinsic motivation* to do the right

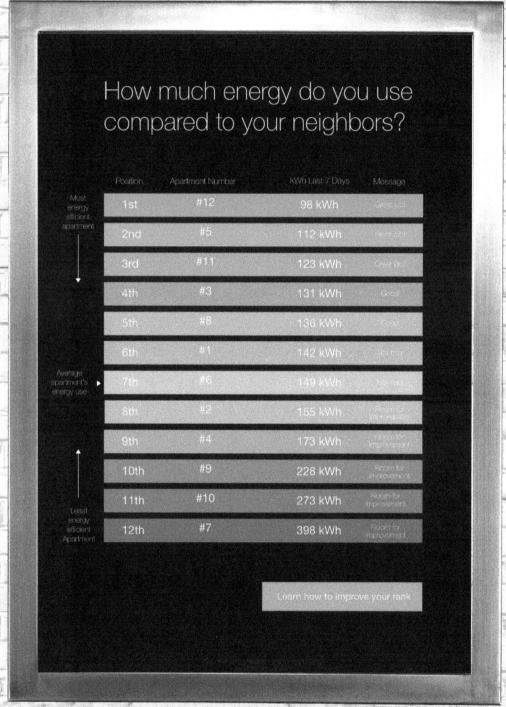

How much energy do you use compared to your neighbors?

	Position	Apartment Number	kWh Last 7 Days	Message
Most energy efficient apartment	1st	#12	98 kWh	Great job!
	2nd	#5	112 kWh	Great job!
	3rd	#11	123 kWh	Great job!
	4th	#3	131 kWh	Good
	5th	#8	136 kWh	Good
	6th	#1	142 kWh	So-so
Average apartment's energy use	7th	#6	149 kWh	So-so
	8th	#2	155 kWh	Room for improvement
	9th	#4	173 kWh	Room for improvement
	10th	#9	228 kWh	Room for improvement
	11th	#10	273 kWh	Room for improvement
Least energy efficient Apartment	12th	#7	398 kWh	Room for improvement

Learn how to improve your rank

Electronic leaderboard: displays the energy that individual apartments use, ranked from least to most energy consumed. Designed by Hello World Labs.

	Bay Area Race to Zero	
1st	San Francisco	1,021
2nd	Contra Costa	1,174
3rd	Santa Clara	1,220
4th	Marin	1,382
5th	Sonoma	1,423
6th	Alameda	1,428
7th	San Mateo	1,450
8th	Solano	1,490
9th	Napa	1,616

Scorecard

#1	Whole Foods	7.45
#2	Wegmans	7.29
#3	Hy-Vee	7.22
#4	Safeway	7.16
#5	Target	6.90
#6	ALDI	6.45
#7	Trader Joe's	6.13
#8	Ahold	6.06
#9	Delhaize	6.01
#10	Meijer	5.55
#11	Giant Eagle	5.06
#12	Walmart	5.47
#13	H-E-B	5.45
#14	Price Chopper	5.26
#15	Costco	5.24
#16	SUPERVALU	5.11
#17	Wakefern	5.10
#18	Kroger	5.03
#19	Albertsons	5.04
#20	WinCo	4.32
#21	Southeastern Grocers	3.26
#22	Roundy's	2.69
#23	Publix	2.61
#24	A&P	1.68
#25	Save Mart	1.44

Low-tech leaderboards: left: ranking the average garbage produced per person per year for counties in the Bay Area, right: Greenpeace scorecard for sustainable food retailers.

thing into tangible behaviors in the real world. You aren't turning people into competitive mercenaries—you are helping people to do a better job of what they already want to be doing, and doing it in a way that is more enjoyable.

It may seem like making a leaderboard is a simple task, but for most environmental and social change indicators, and in many organizations, no leaderboards have been made. You might need to gather data at a level of granularity that hasn't been collected before, such as by street, by building, or by person. It may require installing environmental sensors that collect information such as temperature, pollution, or energy use. You can code up a leaderboard electronically, but leaderboards don't have to be high tech. You can easily make a leaderboard using a spreadsheet of existing data you find in published reports and free graphics programs like canva.com. Using minimal tech skills, you can design it, email it to a list, promote it on social media, and post it to your organization's website. You could even be the first one in your industry to put this information together in a leaderboard design and share it widely, which could have a powerful and exciting effect.

Whichever end of the low-to-high-tech spectrum you fall on, start by gathering your data, ranking your players, and putting this information out there for everyone to see. You'll be surprised by what starts to happen.

COLOR GRADING

Nothing communicates as swiftly as color. If you read a word or see numbers in a table, it takes a little time and energy to interpret, but color alone can often say the same thing instantly. Think of a traffic light. As soon as you see a color like *red, yellow*, or *green*, you instantly and unconsciously identify it as *stop*, *slow*, or *go*. If a traffic light displayed only the numbers *1, 2,* or *3*, or the words *stop, slow*, or *go*, it would take more mental effort to figure out what was going on, and would probably lead to many more crunched up cars.

You can correlate a spectrum of colors to your players' data. A familiar example is the fire danger dashboard. Each degree of fire hazard severity is assigned a color, and we immediately know what it means. Colors naturally trigger an emotional response associated with the player's rank like, *"I'm red, BAD, Why am I red! Yikes, I don't want to be in the red zone!"* or *"I'm green, phew! Great!"*

You can easily start applying color grading to your project. You can purchase graphics templates of dashboard and dial illustrations from stock image websites, you can design your own, or you can just add color to a spreadsheet of data. You can have fun with stickers, too. You can assign people in a team with color-coded stickers based on their performance. I've often thought that cars should have colored stickers on their plates that indicate their fuel efficiency. I think people

The Civic Orb: A concept design by Hello World Labs that displays a city's total real-time energy consumption using a large color-changing spherical light.

Left: Greenpeace Guide to Greener Electronics ranks electronics corporations on the colored graphical dashboard. Right: programmable LED lights to communicate what this data means to your audience in a way that drives them to change.

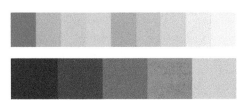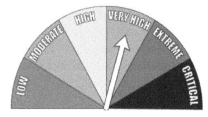

Left: examples of a cool and warm color spectrum you can apply to data. Right: fire hazard dial communicates fire severity using color.

would be deterred from owning a car with a red or crimson sticker on it, even if the sticker is small and hard to see.

The *Ambient Orb* was a spherical light that disclosed a household's energy consumption by glowing red when the home used a lot of energy and glowing cooler colors when the home was using less energy. The makers of the glowing light claimed that it caused people to reduce their energy use by up to forty percent.(20) Forty percent is a *huge* reduction. It worked so well because the glowing colors are *immediate* and easy to understand. The Ambient Orb was superseded by a promising new startup called *GlowEnergy.io* that launched a colored energy light in 2018.

You don't need to keep your use of color in the two-dimensional world. You can build an electronic display using LED lights and an Arduino micro-controller that lights up and flashes in response to your player's performance. With electronic parts you can buy on the internet, you can make something bright, colorful, and wonderful that changes people's behavior, and lights up the world with a data display that is not just meaningful, but beautiful, too.

STAR RATINGS

A star rating provides your players with a score out of five stars. It displays data in a symbolic and simplified way that encourages your player to improve performance. Although the star rating might look simple, don't underestimate its power. A star rating can be especially effective if you can get the government to require it across an entire industry. That's what happened in Australia for the *Energy Stars* system. This program requires that a big sticker with a star rating on it is displayed on appliances such as gas heaters, refrigerators, dishwashers, and even water appliances like taps and shower heads when they are for sale. Since the *Energy Stars* system was introduced, Australian dishwashers use twenty-five percent less water, and air conditioners use half the energy, compared to the same appliances ten years ago, and these improvements are significantly attributed to the star rating sticker.(21) The same thing happened with vehicle safety. Car safety ratings using stars and color have catalyzed the improvement of car and SUV safety design, resulting in a twenty percent rise in safety scores.(22)

You can combine all the design techniques in this chapter for more impact. The car safety star ratings use comparison, color, and stars together to make an instantly intuitive graphic that caused a powerful upward spiral in car safety, and saved thousands of lives.

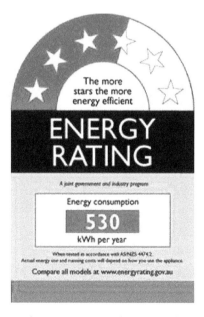

Star rating disclosure: energy and water rating stickers are a mandatory disclosure mechanisms in Australia.

LARGE CARS								
Ford	Falcon FG/FG-X	08-14	★	★	★	★	★	Safe Pick
Holden	Statesman/Caprice WM/WN	06-14	★	★	★	★	★	Safe Pick
BMW	5 Series E39	96-03	★	★	★	★	★	
Holden	Statesman/Caprice WK/WL	03-06	★	★	★	★	★	
Mercedes Benz	E-Class W211	02-09	★	★	★	★	★	
Toyota	Aurion	12-14	★	★	★	★	★	
Holden	Commodore VE	06-13	★	★	★	★		
Mercedes Benz	E-Class W210	96-02	★	★	★	★		
Mitsubishi	380	05-08	★	★	★	★		
Toyota	Aurion	06-12	★	★	★	★		
Ford	Fairlane & LTD AU	99-02	★	★	★			
Ford	Fairlane & LTD BA/BF	03-07	★	★	★			
Ford	Falcon BA/BF	02-08	★	★	★			
Holden	Commodore VY/VZ	02-07	★	★	★			
Holden	Monaro	01-05	★	★	★			
Lexus	ES300/Windom	92-01	★	★	★			
Mitsubishi	Magna TL/TW/Verada KL/KW	03-05	★	★	★			
Nissan	Maxima	06-09	★	★	★			
Toyota	Avalon	00-05	★	★	★			
Volvo	850/S70/V70/C70	92-99	★	★	★			
Ford	Fairlane N & LTD D	95-98	★	★				
Holden	Statesman/Caprice WH	99-03	★	★				
Ford	Falcon AU	98-02	★					
Ford	Falcon EF/EL	94-98	★					
Holden	Commodore VT/VX	97-02	★					
Holden	Statesman/Caprice VR/VS	94-98	★					
Holden/Toyota	Commodore VR/VS/Lexcen	93-97	★					
Mitsubishi	Magna TE/TF/TH/TJ/ Verada KE/KF/KH/KJ/ Diamante	96-03	★					

Left: star ratings on vehicles are quantitative, transparent, comparative, and immediately understandable. Left: star rating on the Zerowastify app that shows how a business' waste compares to that of other businesses.

MAPS

Everything that happens in the world happens in places that are geographically located *on a map*. You can tell a compelling story by illustrating your data on a geographic canvas. You could show which streets in a suburb make the most waste, which blocks in a city have the worst air quality, or which high schools in a district have the hottest asphalt surfaces in summer.

We've only touched the tip of the iceberg of how we can creatively influence the world using maps. You can incorporate all the game design techniques we've been learning: comparison, leaderboards, color, progress bars, star ratings, badges, awards, and even emotive animals within a map design. You can make high-tech maps that show live real-time feedback loops of data for things like air pollution that you can measure as it's happening. You can make a low-tech map on a piece of paper, with seven schools in one district on the map, each with an empty dot. You can visit each school and ask them to sign up to a pledge to give up using plastic straws or start meat-free Monday in the school cafeteria. You'd give each school that signed up a stamp or sticker of accomplishment to fill the dot on the map. A paper map like this a modest and easy thing to do, but you might find it's the missing link that gets people to sign on and *act*.

Most people have deep emotional connections to the land where they live, which gives maps an innate psychological power. Founder of Google Earth

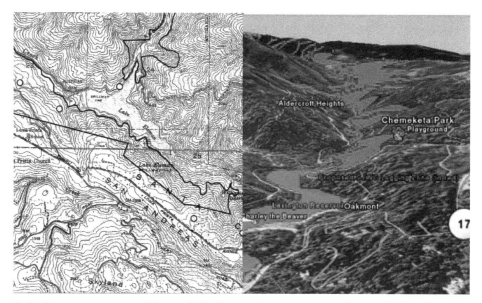

Left: first map sent to residents of the Santa Cruz Mountains showing potential logging zones. Right: Moore's improved map using Google Earth that helped save the forest.

Energy use on a map: this map, created by Columbia University, shows the energy consumption of properties across Manhattan.

Outreach, Rebeca Moore, tells a story of how she used maps to catapult her community into action against a logging proposal near her home in the Santa Cruz mountains. It started when a proposal was mailed out to residents. It contained a simplistic black and white map of the region, but the map was so difficult to understand, and "sketchy" (in Rebecca's words), that local people had hardly been aware that there was any logging planned at all.

Moore remapped the whole thing using Google Earth and was shocked by what she saw. One resident remarked, *"I thought I was well-informed about the proposal to log the watershed. But I nearly fell off my chair when I had a good look at Rebecca Moore's Google Earth presentation of the logging zone. This three-dimensional presentation gave an amazing topographic bird's eye view of how invasive the logging will be."* The new map, by its design, emotionally affected people, and tipped them into action against the logging proposal. Two years later, the forestry plan was abandoned.(23)

Another great mapping opportunity is in energy use. Have you ever wondered where all the energy gets used in a city? A team at Columbia University's Earth Engineering Center worked out how much energy buildings in New York City use.(24) They color-graded the energy consumption data and put it on a map. You can clearly see the areas of high-density energy use. In the future, this project could be developed into a live web application that shows the building's energy use in real-time, and clearly marks which buildings are the best and worst performers, complete with prompts of how the buildings could improve their score.

The NGO, Global Fishing Watch, worked with Google Earth Outreach and image technologists SkyTruth. They created the *Global Fishing Watch Map* which uses satellite photographs to find and track the thousands of big fishing boats that trawl the oceans every day. By monitoring the world's fishing activity, they could see how the Phoenix Islands Protected Area, that was once ravaged by over-fishing, had been successfully left alone to regenerate.(25) Mapping technology proved that environmental legislation worked.

Have you ever thought about where your trash goes once you throw it out? Even the recycled stuff? MIT's *Trash Track Project* attached several hundred GPS trackers to different items of trash—everything from coffee cups to old shoes to computer parts. They put the data on a map that revealed the inefficient and sometimes bizarre movements that discarded items can take. In one sample, a pair of old shoes had been driven all the way across the United States, from Seattle to Florida, and been bounced from multiple waste transfer stations.(26)

Lawrence Berkeley Labs wanted to know how hot the roofs of buildings in cities were getting to gauge their contribution to heating up the whole city. This can be inferred by how much light reflects off a surface in a property called *albedo*. The darker the roof color, the hotter the roof. The lighter the roof color, the cooler the roof. They created the *Roof Albedo Map* project by getting photographs taken by US Department of Agriculture aircraft and applied image processing algorithms to work out the albedo of the roofs on the pictures. The houses with the dark roofs could now be approached or incentivized to paint their roof white or replace it with a lighter colored cool roof.(27)

There are endless opportunities to do interesting things on maps using all the technology ingredients available to us today. Technology products like Google Maps, Google Earth Engine, ESRI, and Mapbox allow you to create all kinds of

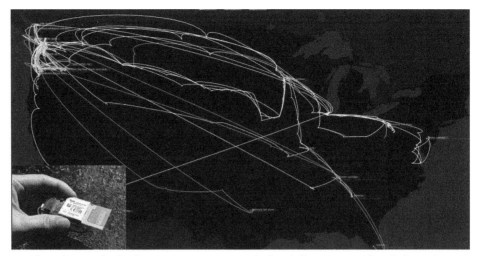

Trash track: Hundreds of GPS sensors were attached to different items of trash, by MIT.

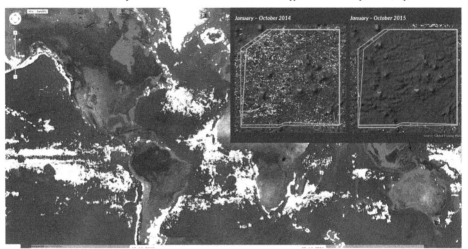

Fishing boat activity: lit up areas indicate fishing boat activity, by Global Fishing Watch.

Roof albedo: mapped the reflectance (its shade of lightness) of roofs, by Berkeley Labs.

visual features, from simple polygons to elaborate animated infographics. You can get satellite images from NASA Earth Observatory or private satellite companies like Planet, Aster, or Spot. You can assign a data point, such as air pollution data, or green cover, to a specific address and compare properties against each other. If you want a low-tech solution, just search for your desired locations on Google Maps and take a screen grab, then import the screen-grab into a graphics program like canva.com or Photoshop and add polygons, icons, or color to your image. How can you tell the story of what you are trying to change on a map? How can you use technology to regularly update the data? How can you make sure your map is designed in a way that gets people to *take action*?

PROGRESS BARS

Progress bars are so commonly used on the internet that you probably think they are not interesting—but don't underestimate them. The three ingredients in a progress bar give it the power to be a revolutionary tool in the craft of world-changing: a quantitative *beginning*, a quantitative *end*, and *tracking the progress* in between.

They create a powerful psychological pull to get your players to complete the tasks or actions assigned to them. The progress bar instills an itch to finish, and clearly broadcasts to everyone involved the distance between your current performance and your goal. It can be designed in all kinds of creative and unusual ways.

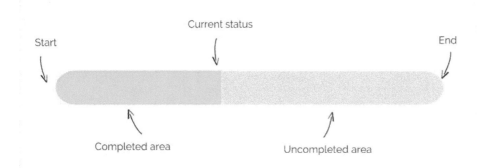

Anatomy of a progress bar: all progress bars have a beginning, a current status, and an end. The colored area indicates current progress.

These three features are a big deal because it's all too common for world-changers to make the mistake of thinking their project is making measurable change, when it isn't (remember Peace Fare guy?). A progress bar at the core of your project will naturally eliminate clumsy ideas that fail to shift the numbers. You can't hide from the progress bar, because it measures *progress*—and *quantitative progress* is all that matters.

Your progress bar probably shouldn't be showing buttons clicked, megabytes downloaded, or arbitrary points gathered, or even money raised—it should go where no progress bar has gone before—deep into the game of tracking, displaying, and changing the Earth's *real-world data*. We need a progress bar that tracks us to zero waste, a progress bar that tracks us to carbon neutrality, a progress bar that tracks us to healthy reforestation. Cities are making carbon neutral goals, sustainable development goals, and healthy city goals all the time, but where are the progress bars that clearly indicate their progress toward these goals? This is a big deal because from what I can see, there is not a single web-based progress bar for any environmental data set anywhere in the world. If you find one, let me know!

I have a cute story about the power of progress bars. One morning at my co-working space in San Francisco, I was talking with my friend Tito. He works on

Progress bar for the Detrashed game: shows the amount of waste the player creates starting at the American national average of 1800 pounds per year. The progress bar moves along as the player moves through the game and commits to taking zero waste actions.

climate change and aspires to bring the spirit of Silicon Valley's ambitious technophilia to the climate movement. I said to him, *"Tito, there are no progress bars for anything in the environmental world. Where is the progress bar for climate change? For air pollution? For waste? The most simple user interface tool that is ubiquitous across the internet has not permeated the world of environmental change. Go on, look it up. Almost no APIs, real-time data, or nice infographics. No progress bars!"*

Tito did go and look it up and he saw what I saw—not much. He got incensed about it and went on to write a blog article called *"No one gives a fuck about climate change"* about the limited visualizations of carbon dioxide from the climate movement. He posted it to Hacker News. The post got 17 upvotes and 10 comments—a feather in the cap for anyone in the startup-hacker scene.

Within 48 hours of the article being posted, five programmers and designers from Europe, America, and Australia had coalesced into a group devoted to rectifying this problem. Without funding, a business plan, or even a leader, they created the website carbondoomsday.com and coded up a feed of atmospheric CO_2 from the NOAA database into a beautifully designed front end. Atmospheric CO_2 can feel distant and confusing, but now through this new interface, it feels (at least a bit more) relatable and understandable. Interacting with numbers on the internet facilitates a sense of *agency* to do something about changing those numbers. For the first time, as a user, you can really interact with, and play with world's climate data, and see how atmospheric carbon dioxide changes considerably from day to day, month to month, and year to year. The group continues to be active on the project today. We don't know yet if carbondoomsday.com will lead to measurable tons of carbon dioxide being removed from the atmosphere, but it has definitely helped the people who view it develop a more intimate bond with climate numbers.

I was excited to see how little it took from my end. All I did was illustrate, in a few sentences, the basic framework of a progress bar: a *beginning*, an *end*, and *progress in between*, and ask, *"Where is the progress bar for climate change?"* This simple question kick-started a chain reaction of human innovation and several hundred hours of volunteer labor. I think progress bars are that powerful that I'm going to ask you to keep asking the same question of every project you work on, *"Is there a progress bar?"* If not, *"How can we create one?"*

The progress bar I designed for the zero waste game *Detrashed* has a starting point of 1800 pounds of trash per person, which is the national average for the amount of waste that one American makes in a year.(12) The end of the progress bar is zero pounds of trash—that's the destination we want our players to reach. As the user moves through the actions in the game, each action is weighted with a

Dot-based progress bar: the Slug Zero game displays progress using yellow dots of varying sizes lying across a forest floor like stepping stones. The user needs to click on the dots, and each dot uncovers a zero-waste action. Dots are sized by the amount of waste the action can save. The user must click on all the dots to reach the next level.

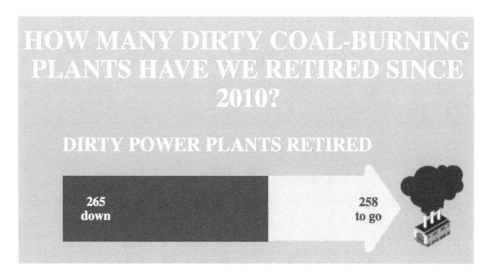

Easy progress bar: The Sierra Club designed this progress bar to show the amount of coal power stations it has helped retire, and how many coal power stations remain active.

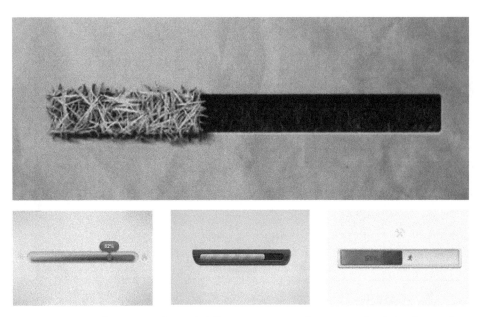

Creative progress bars: use color and different textures such as trees, plastic bottles, or lives saved as a metaphor for what you are trying to change.

particular quantity of trash, measured in pounds. If the player completes all of the actions, he or she eventually reaches zero, indicated by the completion of the progress bar. Components of the *Detrashed* progress bar are:

1) **Beginning:** 1800 pounds
2) **End target:** 0 pounds
3) **Progress:** Wherever the player is from 1800 on the journey to zero.

There's another type of progress bar that is *task-based*. It doesn't move incrementally based on changes in the data. It moves based on completed tasks, chapters, or levels. In the *Slug Zero* game, I added a task-based progress bar to signify progress through the ten levels of the game. The player gets a cute little icon such a banana, rainbow, or mushroom upon completing each level.

You can use the "eat the dots" style of progress bar. It's a bit like how Pacman eats the all the dots to get to the next level. You can visually show the progress you want the player to make in the form of dots that are opened or consumed by the player. In *Slug Zero*, each dot represents a single zero-waste action, and the dots are sized differently depending on how much waste the action can save. The player drags-and-drops the Slug Zero character over each dot in order to open up the zero-waste action.

If you want to build a digital progress bar that automatically updates, you'll need to think about what technology is needed to measure the data, to update the data, and make it visible on the internet through a browser. You can make a low-tech progress bar, too. Get 20 pieces of (recycled) paper, and stick them on your organization's wall. Get a marker, draw a giant progress bar on it. Every week you can update the progress bar by drawing on it. You can create milestones on your progress bar for every five percent it moves and give out rewards, like a free team lunch, or add stickers and write encouraging things on it. Remember, game design is all about feeding the reward center of the brain. We love positive feedback for things we've worked hard for.

Progress bar designs can also be gorgeously creative. You can design them with grass, bubbles, wood, or fire: anything that can look captivating also helps to tell your story. However you make it happen, all you need to do is to make sure you know the numbers about where your players are starting from, and where they're trying to get to. Go forth and dream up new ways to show how you are making progress toward making our world better and keep asking the question, *"Where is the progress bar for . . . .?"* Who knows what incredible things you'll kick off.

BEHAVIOR (STAR) CHARTS

Do you remember using a star chart when you were a kid? Behavior charts, otherwise known as *star* or *sticker charts* are a fun kind of real-world game, and I'm sure you've experienced them already. My mother used to draw up star charts to get me to do lots of things: cleaning, homework. . . . more cleaning. She made one when I was five years old where I got a gold star for every day I stopped sucking my thumb. If I made it to thirty days, I would get a new bicycle. I remember being so excited to get my gold star every day and especially excited when my mother bought me a little lavender-colored bicycle at the end! I love star charts so much that I still use them today for my own personal and business goals, complete with the cutest cupcake stickers I can find.

Behavior charts aren't just for kids. They are a simple and effective way to reward the completion of tasks, levels of achievement, or time-based progress. They keep people motivated and create accountability in the progression towards a goal. They work so well that we can apply them to bigger issues and to influence adult behavior.

The design is simple. You can create a *30 Day Challenge* chart, like the one in the image. It has thirty spots on it and motivational statements inserted along the way. This type of chart is well suited to daily commitments, such as *I composted today, I rode my bike,* or *I didn't use any plastic.* Every time you or your player

196

achieves this goal, you put a sticker on the star chart for that day. If you are trying to influence a large group of people, such as school, a neighborhood, or members of an organization, you can create a behavior chart and distribute it in print or by email.

You can also design a multi-player star chart. You do this by putting the days of the week in the columns along the x-axis, and listing every person's name on the y-axis. This style of chart can be effective if you need to motivate teams of people such as house-mates, employees, or students. You might want to get your co-workers to stop bringing disposable plastic bottles to work, or your roommates to remember to take their reusable bags to the store. Every day, you can give people in the team a sticker, stamp, or star, based on whether they achieved the desired behavior.

I have another cute memory about just how emotionally sticky star charts can be. I had this awful job when I was seventeen years old dressing up as a giant koala and asking for donations for The Wilderness Society in Australian. As much as I cared about trees and wanted to help The Wilderness Society, the job was truly more horrible than even the most horrible job I'd ever had washing dishes in the back of restaurants. The suit was covered in holes, it smelled really bad, and begging for money from people in the city was a mortifyingly depressing way to spend two hours that caused anyone who did it lose all faith in humanity.

There was one thing our koala-leader did that will be forever etched into my memory. Once a week, we had a team meeting where all the koalas came together and we scheduled our shifts and had our performance reviewed. The koala-leader wrote on a large piece of paper on the office wall the amount of money that each koala had earned during their shifts from the previous week. Each koala was assigned silver stars commensurate with the amount of donations she or he had gathered. Usually we'd all get one star, maybe two stars, and sometimes no stars at all.

One week I'd had some good luck, and I got not one, not two, but *three stars!* That meant I was *"STAR KOALA"* for the week! I was the only koala with three stars and the koala-leader wrote on the board for everyone to see, *"Katie Patrick Star Koala!"* and congratulated me in front of all the other koalas. I'd only just finished high school at this stage and I had never won anything or been star of *anything* before. I felt so proud and appreciated that I even kept my *star koala* accolade on my resume for way too many years to come.

Multi-player behavior charts work because they leverage the power of *public accountability*, and it can work wonders. When we attain a goal, or get a reward, like a cherry sticker, or a public display of how we are winning, it makes us feel good about ourselves and creates a positive feedback loop, and consequently a

30-day challenge behavior chart.

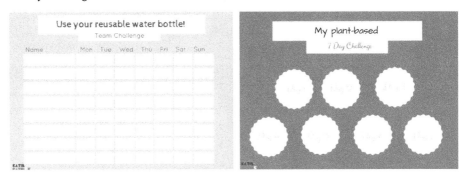

Right: Seven-day team behavior chart. Left: Individual seven day challenge.

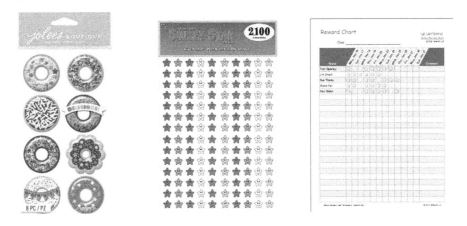

Left: fun stickers you can use. Right: Team-based behavior chart on a calendar.

virtuous upward spiral of more good behaviors. The simple star system requires nothing more sophisticated than a piece of paper and stickers. Yet by its design, it pulls on our psyche's deepest needs for appreciation, goal achievement, and social prestige, and by feeding our desire to be rewarded, it has a remarkably powerful effect.

What can you do to make a fun and creative star chart for your cause? You could make one for really big issues, like the number of coal power stations in your state. You could get a sticker every time you close one down. You could email your members a PDF chart to download and print, similar to the *30 Day Plastic-Free Challenge* example. Even if you are designing something for a corporate client or a government department, don't feel afraid of making it more fun by enhancing the design and choosing more exciting stickers like whales, pandas, strawberries or whatever you think is cool. Use your creativity to inspire action, to engage people with a fun chart, and to activate that special emotional reward mechanism that makes us associate joy with doing good things in the world.

CUSTOM DIGITAL SCREENS

What would your environmental footprint look like if it were displayed on a screen that was attached to the wall? Custom digital screens are a new kind of canvas you can embed into the three-dimensional landscape that has exciting potential. You can use a public-facing screen to display data, color, leaderboards, charts, and rewards like smiley faces, in a way that captivates the attention of passers-by and encourages people to take an action.

The fun thing about digital displays is that you can make them update automatically in real-time. The closer you can get to showing a real-time feedback loop of your data in a way that is public-facing, the more it can instill the sense of *agency* that will drive people to *do something*. They work well for the type of data that is easily measurable by electronic sensors, such as energy, water, or air pollution. You might show the number of cars, cyclists, or boats going by, or the liters of fuel being used by your city in a day.

You can use big screens and small screens. You can program an entire electronic billboard that hangs over a freeway to show your city's real-time carbon emissions. You can use screens that fill the entire wall of a building. You can use small screens the size of a watch, a smartphone, or a desktop monitor. They can be installed in walls, foyers, bus-shelters, elevators, under light switches, beside walkways, or wherever your imagination leads you to put them.

You might be wondering, "Why should we create yet *another* digital screen, when each of us already has a screen on our laptop and smartphone?" It's a concept called *ambient messaging*. It means displaying information in a way that becomes part of the ambient environment so that everyone walking past it, or waiting next to it, absorbs the message *involuntary*. If we see a display screen when we walk through our office foyer, sit down at a bus shelter, or ride in an elevator, we can't really escape what it is telling us.

If you create an app instead of a publicly visible screen, your player will need to download the app, open the app to check it, or open a browser and type it into Google. That's a lot of steps your audience needs to take to see your message. Smartphones and laptops are cluttered with all kinds of messages and notifications, so your app will need to compete with a busy landscape. It could be a dicey gamble to focus solely on a smartphone app. If you want high numbers of people to look at your message, you could be missing out on the vast majority of people you can influence by integrating your message into the everyday built environment.

When it comes to getting your display screen to motivate people to do *behaviors*, timing is everything. Digital screens are best placed in fixed locations where they can communicate a cue to act at the *right time*. Conventional smartphones or laptops can't do this very well. You could put a tiny one-inch screen display underneath every light switch in a home or office. The screen could show the amount of energy the building was currently using with a color grading of crimson, red, orange, yellow, or green, that was proportional to the kilowatts of electricity being used. Color is an especially powerful ambient message to use in public screens, because we can't help but to immediately assign it meaning: red means bad, crimson means *really* bad, green means good. It could even be a single

Digital screens: You can create digital screens that use motivational prompts such as color and rank for personal or outdoor public displays. Raspberry Pi touch screens sell on Amazon for about $40, and large displays from Dell or Samsung start at about $200 per screen.

Public-facing screens: an outdoor public screen that shows air quality using color, disclosure of data, and star ratings. It is designed to measure the air quality in exact locations such as schools, parks, and bus shelters, by being directly attached to an air quality sensor.

The carbon counter screen: a large outdoor public screen that shows global carbon dioxide emissions in real time. Designed by Hello World Labs.

red, orange, or green LED. If you saw a little screen glowing crimson, then you'd be cued to turn the light switch off. The screen gives a signal at the *right time*. It is located in the *right place* to catalyze the desired behavior—to flick off the switch.

Although making your own custom display screen might seem a technically advanced endeavor, it's not out of your reach. You can purchase a Raspberry Pi touchscreen on Amazon for between $20 and $50 that looks like a small tablet.

Touch screen kiosk for University of Santa Cruz student dorms: a leaderboard of waste produced from different dorms displayed on a Dell touch screen. We made an enclosure for the screen using laser-cut 45mm birch plywood. The app was built in React and Node and shown on the screen using a wifi-connected Raspberry Pi.

You can purchase sensors and electronic components from sparkfun.com to help you capture data. To make a touchscreen interface, you need to build a website that looks the way you want the screen to look, that is designed to suit the screen's dimensions. Then you display your website on the screen via a wifi connection. There are many tutorials available on YouTube and on websites like lynda.com, instructables.com, and hackster.io that can teach you how to do it. There is also an abundance of computer programmers and designers you can hire on upwork.com who can help build your idea.

The team at Hello World Labs and I created a beautiful screen installation for the University of Santa Cruz. We used a 24-inch Dell touch screen that cost $300 and a Raspberry Pi that cost $40. We built a website in full-stack javascript that we customized to look nice on the dimensions of the Dell screen. We programmed the Raspberry Pi to display only our website's URL on the Pi's browser, and to show it at full screen, hiding the browser or cursor. The result looked wonderful and it only took a little extra effort. The touch screen display would be seen by thousands of passing students. If we had just left everything on the web, few people would have ever seen it.

There's a giant floor-to-ceiling digital screen in the lobby of the Salesforce Tower in downtown San Francisco. It's programmed to show beautiful and mesmerizing digital artwork and animations. It doesn't show data (especially not real-time data) about important things happening in our city, and on our Earth today. It doesn't show our daily carbon dioxide emissions, how much gasoline we

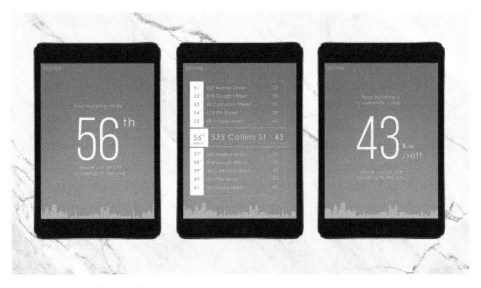

Commercial building public energy displays: a large screen that shows the amount of energy a commercial building uses and automatically updates in real time and displays the building's rank and position against other buildings in the city. Design by Hello World Labs.

use, our city's energy consumption, the changing size of the Earth's glaciers, or the scale of the garbage we throw out each week. Imagine if this enormous digital wall that thousands of people see every day could illustrate the real environmental pulse of the Earth, and when we changed our behaviors, it changed in response. These are the kinds of digital screens I dream about building, and I hope I can inspire you make them, too.

BADGES

Badges are a fun way to reward your player's progress as they move through your game. A badge signifies a level of accomplishment or skill that your player has achieved. Badges generally do not signify *competition* with other players, and that makes them different than awards. You could give a badge out when a player achieves her first ten percent of progress, then again at fifty percent, and at eighty percent, regardless of how the other players are performing.

There is one badge that is the most important of all, and that is your *onboarding* badge. You want to make sure that the *first step* your player takes to get his *first badge* is extremely easy for him to accomplish. This easily-achieved first badge gives your players a reward as early as possible into the journey and helps hook them into the game. You can give badges out to players every time they make it through a designated level of what you are trying to get them to do. Badges help cultivate the player's relationship with their own mastery of the process you are leading them through.

You can use a badge to hook your player's motivation early in their interaction with your project, and help them to stick with you through the whole process. Codeacademy.com is an online interactive computer programming course that uses badges in a fun way. As the student makes her way through the courses, she accumulates many of these colorful badges. I've done several of their tracks and I found these badges boosted my self-esteem after completing the reasonably challenging coding exercises, and helped to hook me in to complete the courses I had started.

Badge designs: codeacademy.com's badges used to mark the student's progress through the learning exercises.

Badge designs: cute badge designs you can purchase online and incorporate into your project to reward users for doing well.

Begin by identifying between five and ten distinct levels of competence or mastery for which you can award badges. You can purchase badge designs from stock image websites like istockphoto.com or iconfinder.com. If you want to take an easy low-tech approach to badges that can work in an office or a school classroom setting, you can give your players fun stickers every time they reach the designated goal.

AWARDS

Awards give people status, improved reputation, and they reward people's effort *in comparison with other players*. They motivate people to continue their efforts because recognition from authorities and peers is important to us. You are probably familiar with the type of physical awards made from glass or steel that are given out at award ceremonies or sporting events. But don't forget that you can use *digital awards*, in the form of computer graphics, and they can be just as powerful a motivator.

A friend of mine ran an interesting case study about the effect of digital awards on volunteer Wikipedia editors. She tested if giving an award, in the form of a digital graphic of a flower, after the volunteer had reached a number of hours influenced the amount of time the volunteers contributed to editing Wikipedia pages. Her study found that adding the purely symbolic award increased the share of active editors by twenty percent.(28) The flower also had a striking emotional effect on those who received it, with contributors making comments like this, *"Thank you very much for the recognition, I will continue contributing,"* and *"I feel very honored to receive this award! It makes me realize that contributions, even if they may be small, are recognized here."* A twenty percent improvement that came about just by giving editors a digital flower is a big increase for such a small feature.

The website *Psychological Science* tested the result of giving authors a digital award. The site provided its contributing authors with a badge when they designated their publications as "open data," meaning that the manuscript was made publicly available. The introduction of the badges caused a jump from three to twenty-three percent of authors making their publications open, which is a multiple of thirteen times.(29) It jumped even more, to thirty-nine percent, the following year. These huge numbers are achieved just by adding a simple graphic. It costs little, if anything at all, to add these digital awards to an app or website, but they can result in substantial wins.

Another study on charitable donations tested the effect that positive statements

Put a cherry on it
Congratulations!
You composted today!

Rainbows for you
Great job, you've composted 5
days in a row!

Robot dance
Perfect streak! Like a robot of finely
tuned skill, you've composted
perfectly for 21 days in a row!

Polar bear of force
You've accumulated 50 days of
composting, that's so much you've
probably saved a polar bear's life!

Mount sustainability
You've accumulated 100 days of
composting! You've climbed mount
sustainability!

Badges, meaning and emotion: You need to decide at what level of progress you will provide your player with a badge. Your player will emotionally connect with your badges if you give them fun names and descriptions.

had on people who were donating money to the Heart Association. Those who were thanked by a human being after giving a donation and told, *"You are a generous person. I wish more of the people I meet were as charitable as you"* gave seventy-five percent more when asked to donate to another charity.(30) This case study doesn't provide the subjects with a physical or digital award, but it can be interpreted as a kind of verbal award and it tells a story of how meaningful it is to have our efforts appreciated. Any way you can weave signs of appreciation into your project using graphical, physical, or verbal awards has the potential to unleash these kind of results.

You can use the *award concept* in a new and novel way that *does create change.* I think the award concept can be dramatically reinvented to reward people based on how much real environmental data they shift. You can start giving awards out to the family in a neighborhood that used the least amount of water in a year, or to the lowest environmental footprint house, or to the school that made the least amount of waste in your state, or corporate headquarters that most reduced their energy use. Using an award in the context of real-world, data-driven gamification is quite different than the lavish corporate award ceremonies you might be used to, but probably fail to create any real and measurable change, even if they are environmentally or socially themed. This data-centric type of award encourages the upward spiral of change in a way that people can be proud of.

EMOTIVE ANIMALS

You can add cute animal avatars or mascots, such as pandas, whales, crabs, birds, or even slugs to your design, and add evocative expressions to the faces of your critters. It works because emotions displayed on the face of an illustrated animal can trigger the user's emotional response.

In case you were thinking that emotive pictures of animals are silly, let's look at a case study that added a cartoon owl to a multiple choice learning game. The researchers tested two owls: one owl with a smile, and the other owl with no discernible expression. The addition of the smiling owl increased the student scores by twenty-three percent, compared to students that got the owl with no facial expression.(31) Twenty-three percent is a *big uptick* in performance, just by adding a single happy owl to the project. It's an easy add-on that anyone can do.

What is interesting about the owl experiment is the *mechanism* for how the happy owl influenced the students' scores. The presence of the smiling owl increased the student's level of happiness and general positivity towards the game —the student *mirrored* the happy emotion of the owl. With a happier attitude, students were able to be more engaged with the learning experience, which kept them concentrating longer, and ultimately led to their increased scores. Think of

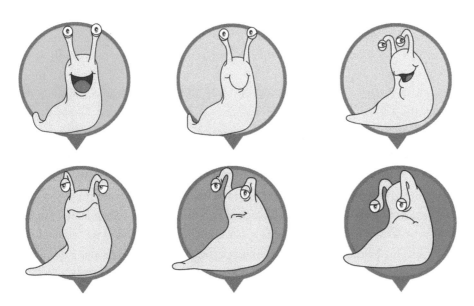

Emotive slugs: Each slug has an emotional expression based on the dorm's position on the university's waste leaderboard. This design combines the techniques of emotive animals with color grading, leaderboards, and maps. Each dorm is assigned a banana slug with a color and an emotional expression commensurate with the dorm's quantity of waste produced.

your emotive animal as a kind of "mood booster" that will keep people engaged with your material.

All of our actions are ultimately driven by *emotion*. Emotions signal to the brain that *an action* needs to be taken. If something makes you feel happy, you want to move closer to it. If something makes you feed bad, you will probably move away from it. We also want to emotionally connect with other beings, we all love animals, and we all love to have fun.

I noticed this effect when people interacted with the zero-waste interface I designed for the University of Santa Cruz. The team recommended that I feature the banana slug (the school's official mascot) as the emotive animal of choice. We designed seven different slugs, each to show an expression, from ecstatic to deflated, and presented them to the users based on how much waste the student dorm had produced.

If you are not already familiar with the banana slug, it is a bizarre bright yellow slug that lurks amongst the fallen leaves of California's redwood forests. The UCSC students *adore* it. They adore the banana slug so much that the students actually broke out into protest one year when the chancellor tried to switch their beloved mascot to a more stately animal.(32) I tell this story to illustrate the deep attachment we can cultivate to imaginary caricatures of fauna—even slugs. Think of ewoks, ET, gremlins—our emotional connection to imaginary animals is real.

The project hasn't been up long enough to say if the emotive slugs are directly influencing the students to make less waste, but everyone who looks at it says something like, *"Aww cute slug! That's so cool. Oh poor slug, he's not doing so well."* I see their expression mirror the slug they are looking at, and sparks of emotion burst out in a way that you just don't see when you show someone a chart of data.

Creativity doesn't need to be difficult or expensive. It cost $117 to hire an illustrator on upwork.com to draw the emotive slugs. Then it took me about three hours to add them to the app. There's no reason to restrict the type of fun you can have with your social change designs. When we apply creativity, not randomly, but guided by robust theories for change, we can get a lot closer to getting our projects to save the world, and have a great time doing it.

This game design chapter has explored visual features you can use to bond people to your cause and your numbers. But there's more to the game than what it *looks* like. Now it's time to weave together the *story* that your player will move through. You are taking a human being on a journey, and through an experience. The next chapter will help you do just that.

STEP #8A: GAME DESIGN EXERCISE

1. Players: Decide on who your players will be. They can be individual people, businesses, departments, cities, suburbs, states, streets, colleges, houses, dorms, students, or corporations. Create a spreadsheet with your players in one column and their performance data on what you are trying to achieve in the next column.

2. Data literacy: Think of how you can enhance your player's data literacy about your cause. Can you make a poster with your numbers on it?

3. Feedback loop: Work out how you can gather and update your data more frequently. How can you reduce the latency in your feedback loop? How will you use your feedback loop to signal to your player to change a behavior? How will you get your player's attention? How will you reward the player after he or she makes a change?

4. Comparison: Create a graphic that shows how your player compares with other similar players. You can use visual representations of data, such as the size of objects, a bar chart, or a 1st-2nd-3rd podium design.

5. Leaderboards: Create a leaderboard by ranking your players from best to worst. You can find a leaderboard design on istockphoto.com, design one yourself using canva.com, or contract a graphic designer to create one for you. Make your leaderboard publicly visible and distribute it to your players.

6. Color: Choose a color scheme with gradations that correlate with your data. Apply your color scheme to each of your players and to each of the gamification features you use like stars or maps.

7. Star ratings: Decide on what numerical criteria you will use to allocate star ratings to your players. Create a visual design that utilizes the star rating in an app design, sticker, or clothing tag.

8. Maps: Show your players on a Google or Mapbox map using pins, custom markers, polygons, and color grading.

9. Progress bars: Create a progress bar by determining the data point that indicates where your player is starting from, and where he will end his journey. Think through how you can update your progress bar as your players make progress towards their goal.

10. Digital screens: Purchase a screen such as a Raspberry Pi or Dell touchscreen. Program your screen to display your web application. Position the screen in a public location, in the most optimal place where it can influence your player's behavior. Program your screen to automatically update the data in response to your player's actions in a feedback loop.

11. Badges: Identify between five and ten distinct levels of progress or mastery for which you can award badges. Create an onboarding badge to reward your player's first (easy) win.

12. Awards: Decide at what point in your player's journey, or at what rank she needs to attain, you will provide the award. Devise a system to give the award to a player when she reaches that point.

13. Emotional avatars: Decide how you want to reward or influence your players with emotional animal avatars. You might choose a couple of different faces to express happy, sad, lost, or confused emotions.

14. Promote it: Get your gamification designs out there for people to see! Put them on your website, on a big poster on the wall, post them on social media, and email them to your members.

15. Fun and novel: Does your concept pass the test of being interesting? Is it fun? Is it boring? Is it novel? Does it make people smile? Does it make people want to learn more?

16. Design: Find designs for badges, awards, animals avatars from istockphoto.com, iconfinder.com, or shutterstock.com. Design them yourself in canva.com or Adobe Illustrator.

Who is the mentor?
You.

Who is the hero?
Your audience.

STEP #8B

TELL YOUR STORY

"Until the lion learns how to write, every story will glorify the hunter."
— African proverb

You know why your cause is important. You might have even been moved to tears by it. But does everyone else know why your cause matters? You need to tell the story to other people, too. But not just any story. You need to tell a story that is so captivating that your words lift your audience out of time and place and weave a sparkling thread of inspiration through their hearts and up into their minds. Then with that delicate thread, you pull them close to you, and to your cause. Can you craft a story that gives people butterflies, and that stirs a deep curiosity in them that awakens *their dream* for a better world? A dream that stays with them, not just for an hour, not just for a day, but for a lifetime? You may have heard of *the power of story*. It's a real tool, and it's a skill that can be learned.

There is a simple story-telling template called *The Hero's Journey*. It's a twelve-step structure that can be applied to any topic, in any format. It works for everything from a short "about us" page to a big Hollywood feature film. You can even use it to tell a compelling story about something as simple as a cheese sandwich, which we'll go into a bit later. In fact, every time I deviate from *The Hero's Journey* structure, my story starts to feel like a mismatching pair of shoes, and people give me awkward feedback like, "*Err, I like that bit, maybe take the other bit out, it's pretty good, but ummm . . . I'm not sure. Great job though!*" When I go back and restructure it to fit into *The Hero's Journey* template, I get *this kind* of feedback, "*It changed my life, I have tears in my eyes writing this. Thank you for putting this in the world.*" It's striking. Your ability to resonate with the human soul has got nothing to do with the topic. It has everything to do with your *story template.*

The Hero's Journey was popularized by Joseph Campbell in his 1949 book, *The Hero with A Thousand Faces*. Campbell talks about the concept of the "monomyth," which is a singular story structure that has been told over and over again in stories throughout the ages. Most stories that have passed the test of time are in fact pretty similar. *The Hero's Journey* works because it is a template of the human experience and, in my opinion, it's reflective of the basic psychological framework of how we interpret the world around us.

Do you remember that famous "*Red pill or the blue pill*" scene from the movie *The Matrix*? It's an iconic visual metaphor for *step five* in the process: *crossing the threshold*. Big epic films like *Star Wars, Lord of the Rings*, and *The Matrix* all use *The Hero's Journey* and, like the red-pill-blue-pill scene, they use very specific mile-markers in the film that signify when the story jumps from one phase to the next.

There's a critical preliminary step to take when you are getting ready to tell a nonfiction story. You start by defining two characters: *the hero* and *the mentor*. I like to call this process *Turning the mirror around*. Have you seen those TEDx talks when the speaker opens with a childhood picture of himself? It's cringe-worthy, right? Don't do that. Don't tell your own life story, with the *actual story* you are trying to tell speckled in like raisins in a cookie. You are not the hero in the story you are trying to tell. *You are the mentor*. The hero is the *audience*. The hero is the player, the reader, or the user.

Nancy Duarte in her book *Resonate* explains it with Luke Skywalker as the hero (that's your audience) and Yoda as the mentor (that's you: the storyteller, and the expert). Your job is to guide your hero through *their own adventure* to another possible world, into the darkest parts of themselves, and face-to-face with their quest for beauty, truth, and meaning, or whatever quest they are taking.

There are two main pillars that support your story: *intention* and *obstacle*. The *intention* is the thing your hero wants or the place he wants to go. The *obstacle* is the challenge that stands in the way. In the chasm between these two things, your dramatic story emerges. By going through it, your hero will experience a *transformation*. Your job, as *the mentor*, is to meet your hero in his current *ordinary world* and take him on a journey into *another world* that changes him forever and leaves him as a new and better person.

As you go through the twelve steps, *The Hero's Journey* will force you to ask the difficult question of *why?* It's easy to tell a story about objective scientific or environmental facts, and assume that people *ought to care* about the topic as much as you do. But there is much more to the human experience that connects us to the causes we are involved in. *The Hero's Journey* will force you to dig deeply into the personal and spiritual drivers that *move us to care.* This is where you will ask, and answer, how your hero's most important philosophical questions about meaning, purpose, suffering, love, and identity are connected to your cause. Your job is to tell a story that transforms the reader from her normal and ordinary self, and confronts her with the inner reason that is keeping her from breaking through to the other side of everything she wants to be.

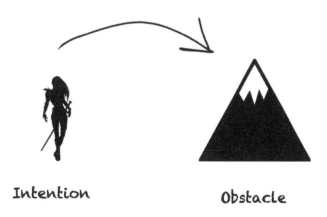

Intention   Obstacle

Hero's transformation

Intention and obstacle: a dramatic narrative occurs when you have a hero that has an intention that is blocked by an obstacle. The hero makes a transformation as she tries, fails, and eventually overcomes the obstacle.

Discovering *The Hero's Journey* profoundly changed the way I communicate, and even changed my whole life. As I tried to answer the deeper questions in the twelve steps, I found they were pretty tough to answer. I mean, *why* should someone care about the billions of disposable coffee cups in landfills? What deep *inner shift* does someone need to make to turn from a person who mindlessly consumes and throws away plastic into someone who is deeply conscientious and mindful of the environmental footprint of every little thing he buys? What do I have to uncover inside a person's soul to fundamentally change the way he thinks about the world and about himself? This is a much harder story to tell than talking about gazillions of tons of plastic in the ocean.

While pondering these questions, and also searching for academic studies to help me find the answers, I discovered the field of *environmental psychology*. It opened up a new chapter of my life, that led ultimately to the creation of this book. I'm quite sure that I would not have been doing what I'm doing now if I hadn't had my consciousnesses cracked open by following the steps in *The Hero's Journey*, that got me asking *"why?"* at a deeper level than I had ever asked before, and got me grappling with some of life's biggest questions in the context of how I go about trying to save the world. As you use it to tell your story, you'll need to answer these deeper questions, too.

HOW TO DO IT

The twelve steps in *The Hero's Journey* formula will help distill the power and essence of your story in a way that rapidly captures your audience. Write an answer to each of the twelve questions below in one sentence, or just a few short sentences. This gives you the basic framework to get your story started. Remember, you are telling the story from the *audience's* (the hero's) perspective— that means you will use the word "you" a lot, and use the words "I" and "my" as little as possible. Write down what your hero will *experience*. I'll use an example of a cheese sandwich to illustrate how you can tell a profound story about the simplest of things.

1. Ordinary World
In this step, you set up an emotional connection with the hero by showing empathy for the hero's current situation. You do this *before* sharing your idea. Show that you understand her. What is your hero's day-to-day life like? What problem or opportunity is your hero, or the whole world, experiencing right now? What is the hero struggling with in the absence of your idea?

Example: You like to eat things. Most other people like to eat things, too. There's one thing you especially like to eat: a cheese sandwich. But you hear all this conflicting information: what's bad for you, what's good for you, what will give you cancer, all the plastic in the ocean, the melting glaciers. It's confusing and overwhelming to make sense of what we should eat, even for the best of us.

2. Call to Adventure

In this step, you outline the vision for another possible world. Show the hero a unique idea that can make her dreams come true. Illustrate the gap between her life now and this new possible world. What is the destination you are promising that will change everything for your hero? What would the world be like if your idea came true? What kind of life or adventure could your hero have by embracing your idea? Don't divulge the idea yet though! That comes later.

Example: The cheese sandwich is a common food, some might even argue it's an uninteresting food. You've probably never thought deeply about a cheese sandwich, but what if I told you there is one simple answer to all those difficult questions? What if I told you that there is a secret in the cheese sandwich that could transform your relationship with your body, with food, and it could even change the world? What if I told you that inside the cheese sandwich lies one of the greatest social revolutions of our time?

3. Refusal of the Call

In this step, you acknowledge the doubts and fears your hero might be having. You've just made a bold statement, so it's natural your hero is thinking through why it might not work, and what it might cost her. Again, this step shows empathy for the hero's decision-making and helps put your hero at ease to stay with you on the journey. Briefly outline the reasons why your hero might turn away, or think your vision sounds crazy or unviable. Acknowledge those reasons with humility, but explain that your hero doesn't need to worry. You don't need to answer the objections now; we answer them in later steps.

Example: You might think that sounds crazy. How could the cheese sandwich sitting on my table right now possibly change the world? You might think, "I'm just one person, with one sandwich."

4. Meet the Mentor

Now that you've primed the hero's curiosity, this is where you introduce yourself. Your aim here is to establish trust and credibility with the hero. You will let your hero know why *you* are the right person to lead her through the journey. Who are you? What are your qualifications? Why should she trust you? Explain why you are passionate about this cause and why it moves you.

Example: My name is Elizabeth and I'm really good at making cheese sandwiches. I'm so good at it, in fact, that I won the International Cheese Sandwich-Making Award in 2012. I've spent the past fifteen years studying the social, health, and environmental impacts of the dairy industry. I love to eat food, but most of all, I love the Earth, and love being healthy enough to enjoy it. I see the intersection of these three things: food, the planet, and our bodies, as one of the most fascinating frontiers of our time.

5. Cross the Threshold

In this step, we invite the hero to step on board with us and dive fully into the story, into the transformation, and come with us into the other world. This is the red-pill-blue-pill moment from *The Matrix,* and it's the part in *Lord of the Rings* when Frodo leaves The Shire. Make a statement inviting the hero to learn more, or to come with you on the journey. You can frame it in terms of helping her dreams come true, defeating an enemy, or making it to the promised new world.

Example: Just like a journey of a thousand miles starts with a single step, this revolution begins with a single bite. Come with me and let me show you how you can change your life, and change the world, with a bite of your very own cheese sandwich.

6. Tests, Allies, and Enemies

In this step, you illustrate a small battle and a small win. Add more details and facts behind your idea or cause here. Explore the main issues behind why your idea matters. Reveal the work and hurdles involved. What are you up against? Who is your enemy? Who is your friend? What wins has your movement had? What does your hero need to do to make her first small win on her quest?

Example: Let me pull back the curtain on what's really going on behind your cheese sandwich. There are two types of cheese sandwiches in the world. One is made from animal ingredients, and the other is made from plants. These two sandwiches are in a race. They might even be at war. The animal-based sandwich has a disturbing past. Animal agriculture accounts for five times the greenhouse gases of all the world's aircraft. Every day, four billion female cows are locked up in factory farms. Animal fats are the biggest killer in first world countries—a trend that's quickly seeping into Asian and African countries. Cheese sandwiches made from cow's milk have reached a crisis proportion that we are sustaining only at great cost. But now

The Hero's Journey

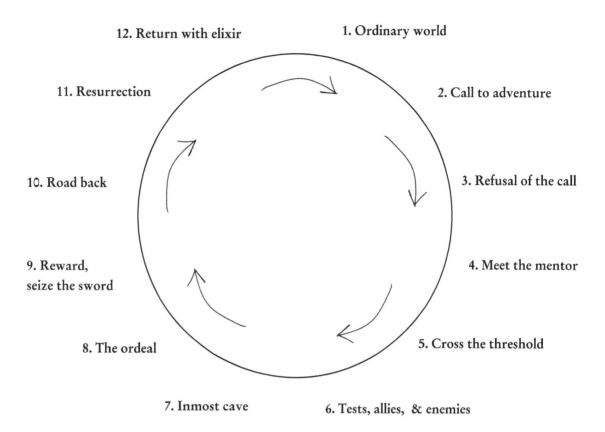

12. Return with elixir   1. Ordinary world

11. Resurrection   2. Call to adventure

10. Road back   3. Refusal of the call

9. Reward, seize the sword   4. Meet the mentor

8. The ordeal   5. Cross the threshold

7. Inmost cave   6. Tests, allies, & enemies

technology has changed everything. Food scientists have learned how to make a cheese sandwich without using animals at all. The cheese is pretty similar, but it's made from ingredients like coconut oil, yeast cultures, and almonds. Not a single cow suffered. It's made little contribution to climate change. It's unlikely to give you heart disease or make you put on weight. In the race between sandwiches, which one will win? The plant-based cheese sandwich makes up only 1.3 percent of the market. It's a David and Goliath battle.

7. The Inmost Cave

In this step, you need to underpin your hero's courage and commitment to keep going. Epic commitment doesn't happen all in one go. What scenario will emerge where your hero comes face to face with their determination to push forward? What new skills does your hero need to learn in order to keep going? Why does this cause or idea matter so much that she should suffer for it? What is it deep inside her soul that will keep her moving forward?

Example: You're still wondering, "Is it really my responsibility to save the world? Those other vegan cheeses don't quite taste the same. Sometimes, they're more expensive. Could I be bothered to try so hard? People at work make fun of my weird vegan food." To change the world, we need to make a choice. Until recently we didn't have the choice of two cheese sandwiches, we had only one. What we eat defines us. When you're at the store, when you're hungry, when you're at a picnic or a meetup, think about which side you are on. Which sandwich will you support? We can't control the bad things that go on in the world, but we can control how we respond to them. In every bite lies your choice and your vote for what kind of world you want. In our choices we wield our power.

8. The Ordeal

In this step, your hero will make a big leap forward, but she won't win the first time. As with all things we do for the first time, there will be an unexpected loss, sacrifice, or setback. What does it take for your hero to continue on and push through hard times?

Example: You make the choice. You bat for the little guy. You chew past the slightly different taste, absorb the sometimes higher price tag, go to the different store where it's sold, and you do it. But what happens when the novelty wears off? When you're the only one you know doing it? What happens when your boyfriend hates it on the pizza, or you're mother criticizes you for wasting money on it or the company chef rolls her eyes at you for complicating the food ordering?

9. Reward, Seize the Sword

In this step, your hero will get discouraged and consider giving up on her idea, but then begin to see some benefit from her efforts. This is when you help her reach the moment of courage it takes to fully commit to the change. What is pulling your hero down? What rewards will she get from pushing through? What losses does she mourn? What's the moment when she comes face to face with the hardest thing?

Example: Then one day, you're tired and hungry, and you're asked if you want cheese on your vegetarian burrito. You couldn't be bothered trying. You want to say yes. Inside of you lies that choice again. It's a choice that shouldn't really be that hard, but sandwiched between a bad day, and a cheese craving, saying "no" is suddenly the hardest thing in the world. Who are you at this very moment? You remember the choice and remember how much better you've been feeling. In that exhausted moment in time and space, you see your actions are a part of history, your part in the David & Goliath battle of the cheeses. It's not that you chose to sacrifice yourself to the cause of the vegan cheese, but that you choose to put your own values first. You come face to face with the secret to self-esteem—that everything you do in practice is in line with what you believe, that you don't flake out on who you are when it gets tough.

10. Road Back
In this step, your hero decides to continue on with a renewed conviction, even though there is resistance around her everywhere. This is the final place where your hero has reached her full and total empowerment.

Example: You've done it. It's easy for you now. You influence people around you to give up the toxic world of dairy products and eat more plants. When you eat, and when you shop it's all plants, all the way. Your friends are inspired by you. You're a beacon of good eating.

11. Resurrection
In this step, you show the hero's new mastery of her new skills and tools. She tries one final time to push the idea forward and is victorious. The hero has left behind her old self, and she is now a new self. There has been some loss, but also a substantial gain. What inner truth has your hero found in the struggle? How is the hero now a new person? How is your hero influencing others?

Example: You've become someone new. You're capable of deeper self-reflection that isn't just about food anymore. It permeates every corner of your life. You shed the skin of someone who accidentally supported the cruelty of animal agriculture. This mindfulness about choosing foods that are made from plants, and not animals, moves into the way you move your body, it opens up new friendships, a new love of life and a new connection to the Earth. The action that used to take willpower, is replaced by effortless happiness—a centeredness in how you live, eat, and shop by your values. By being more sensitive to feeling the suffering of the world, you've also opened up your sensitivity to beautiful experiences. Caring, is two sides of the same coin. When you can care a bit more for everything around you, the world opens up and cares more for you.

12. Return with the Elixir
In this step, you illustrate the utopian happy ending. You take the hero to arrive in the new world. The big idea is adopted and the universe is a better place. How has your hero personally helped make this world come true? How will your hero now become the mentor to others?

Example: Humanity has been getting better with every generation. We've grown out of our infancy where we hurt each other, where we hurt animals, and hurt the planet. We've grown out of the horrors of animal agriculture, of our body-hatred, and collapsing the ecosystem. We figured it out. It's not just the physical world. In order to make this change, we had to change our culture, and with that, change ourselves. The future is made of a trillion tiny choices, including yours. You know that when people look back on the war of plant vs animals foods and the battle takes its place amongst the great wars in history, you had a place in it. That one little action that you committed to every day tapped away, just like everyone else like you tapping at something they believe in, and made a groove that unleashed the river of change. You won the revolution with a bite.

You can see from the cheese sandwich story example that the questions asked in *The Hero's Journey* forced us to get deep. Just writing a blog post about why dairy is *bad* and vegan cheese is *good* might have turned out okay, but probably a bit flat, and it would join the other "preaching to the converted" articles that vegans share with each other on social media. A good story will bring tears to your eyes when you tell it on stage, and to your audiences when they hear it. We're not writing Wikipedia pages here—that's what Wikipedia is for. If you're in the game of changing the world, then what you work on *is profound*, and you can tell it in a way that soars.

STEP #8B: STORY EXERCISE

Write out at least one sentence for each step in *The Hero's Journey*, with your player, customer, user, or target audience as the hero, and you as the mentor.

1. Ordinary world: What is going on in your hero's current world?

2. Call to adventure: What is the quest, problem, new world, or shift that piques your hero's attention?

3. Refusal of the call: What objections might your hero be having and how do you answer them?

4. Meet the mentor: How can you convince your hero that you are experienced, credible, and trustworthy enough for her to follow you?

5. Cross the threshold: How do you invite your hero to commence the journey with you?

6. Tests, allies & enemies: What is a small test you can give your hero that he or she can accomplish, and thus experience a "win"? Who are your hero's friends? Who are your hero's enemies?

7. Inmost cave: What is the deepest inner struggle your hero will face on her journey?

8. The ordeal: What is the biggest struggle your hero will go through? What will she get when she wins? What will be lost in the process?

9. Reward, seize the sword: What big commitment does your hero need to make to make the final big win?

10. Road back: How does your hero continue on with enthusiasm despite setbacks?

11. Resurrection: How has your hero been reborn into someone new?

12. Return with elixir: What is your utopian happy ending?

STEP #9

TRIBES & TIPPING POINTS

"Things don't just diffuse in human populations at random. They actually diffuse through networks." — Nicholas Christakis, Professor of Medicine at Harvard University

Our behavior is directly influenced by the actions and words of people around us. It starts at the very beginning of our lives. If you've ever spent time with a toddler, you would have noticed that they copy everything you do. It's hard to explain *with words* to a two-year-old, how to unscrew a bottle, rotate a puzzle piece, or how to put her foot on the lever that opens the trash can. The only way to teach a two-year-old how to do something is to *show her*. Then for better or worse, she imitates you.

As adults, we're pretty much the same. Just about every dimension of what we do—our behaviors, political views, music preferences, favorite clothes, and sub-cultural slang—is all a reflection of what we see our friends and close ones doing around us. It's such an automatic response that we're hardly aware of how much we imitate others. This means that when you're designing for social change, you want to design your project in a way that hooks into the deeply *social nature* of our being to imitate others. It means that instead of putting all your efforts into approaches to influence people such as pushing facts, using fear-based messages, or trying to pass more legislation, you can allocate some energy to simply *showing people by example* what you want them to do. It's easy to do, and like many good behavior-change techniques, it isn't done nearly enough by people who are trying to change the world.

SOCIAL DIFFUSION

Humans copy the behaviors of other humans around them through a process called *social diffusion*. It's a process whereby social phenomena spread in a similar way to a virus: through social channels, family members, and within groups. It's interesting how we underestimate how strong this influence is on us. A study conducted on what people *think* influences them found that social norms (what

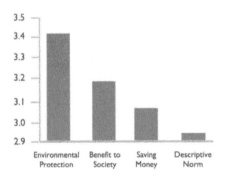

We are wrong about what we think motivates us: This chart tested what kind of messages people assume will affect them. People *think* that they are influenced highly by messages about "environmental protection," followed by messages about "benefits to society," and then "saving money." People presume that descriptive norms are the least likely to affect them. When these messages are put to the test, it's found that people are influenced in the opposite order.

People imitate others: college men in group showers were unresponsive to a sign that said, "Please turn shower off while lathering to save water." When an actor was tasked with displaying the water-saving action, 49 percent of men adopted the behavior.(2)

other people are doing in a group) were voted as the *least* likely way people thought they were affected. But when it's put to the test, many studies show that social norms actually come up as *the most* powerful influencer on people's measurable behavior.(1)

PhD psychologist Doug McKenzie Mohr coined the term *"community-based social marketing"* to describe the practical application of social influence to environmental change projects. An interesting example of *leading by example*, is how male students use water in communal showers. A sign was placed in a college gym shower that said, *"Please help to save water by turning the shower off while you are soaping up."* The students were unresponsive to the sign and continued to keep the water running. The researchers added a student actor to the mix. The student actor's job was to enact the desired behavior in real life and turn the water off while he was soaping up. After getting the actor to passively model this behavior to the group, the other young men unconsciously copied the behavior and it shot up to 49 percent of students adopting the water-saving action. It even reached a higher adoption rate of 67 percent when two actors were used.(2)

The phenomenon of social imitation is found in the social networks of obese people. The habits that cause obesity, such as poor diet and low exercise, follow social diffusion patterns, in just the same way as when we hear about a new band, catch the flu, or buy a new iPhone for the first time. A study conducted on 12,000

NORMS & TOWELS

One of the most well-known studies that reveals how responsive we are to the actions of people around us tested three different kinds of messages on people who were staying in hotel rooms.(3) Laundering towels uses up a lot of water and energy, so there are big environmental gains to be made by hotels encouraging people to use the same towel a few times over.

First message: *"HELP SAVE THE ENVIRONMENT. You can show your respect for nature and help save the environment by reusing your towels during your stay."* **34%**
This message was reasonably successful and got guests to increase their towel reuse rates by 34 percent.

Second message: *"JOIN YOUR FELLOW GUESTS IN HELPING TO SAVE THE ENVIRONMENT. Almost 75 percent of guests who are asked to participate in our new resource-saving program do help by using their towels more than once.* **44%** *You can join your fellow guests in this program to help save the environment by reusing your towels during your stay."*
You'll notice that this second statement refers to the *actions of other people*. It is setting an example that people can imitate, using a technique called *social norms*, or more specifically *descriptive norms*. This second message caused 44 percent of towels to be reused, just by adding these few words that described what everyone else was doing. The researchers didn't stop there though. They added another variation to the message that included the hotel room number. You can see from this example that adding the room number tightens the relationship of the current guest to the previous guests.

Third message: *"JOIN YOUR FELLOW GUESTS IN HELPING TO SAVE THE ENVIRONMENT. In a study conducted in Fall 2003, 75 percent of the guests who stayed in this room (###) participated in our new resource-saving program by using their towels more than once. You can join your fellow guests in* **48%** *this program to help save the environment by reusing your towels during your stay."*
The success rate of this message jumped even further, to 48 percent. That's a fourteen percent improvement, jumping from 34 percent of towels reused, to 48 percent, just by changing a few words. If the third and most successful message were rolled out across several global hotel chains, this small change in words could lead to a sizably reduced environmental footprint.

people over 30 years, showed how obesity spreads through social networks, from person to person via people's relationships with friends, siblings, spouses, and neighbors. The study revealed the pattern in obesity appeared to be "catching" over time. A person's chances of becoming obese increased by 57 percent if he or she had a friend who became obese. If one sibling became obese, the chance that the other would become obese increased by 40 percent. If one spouse became obese, the likelihood that the other would become obese increased by 37 percent. (4) The study was careful to rule out the case of people simply being friends with others of the same body size. The findings of the study showed that obese people are socially clustered together by their close personal relationships, as are non-obese people. It happens because people *copy each other's behaviors*. If someone close in your life starts to become heavier than you, you're likely to copy his eating habits and become heavier, too. Behaviors are catching.

These studies teach us that providing *information* and *education* to try and get people to change isn't the best arrow to strike at the heart of what gets human beings to do things. We need to look at the social context of the behavior and do what we can, even if all we have is a few words to work with, to get people to copy each other. You need to look into your target audience's social connections like

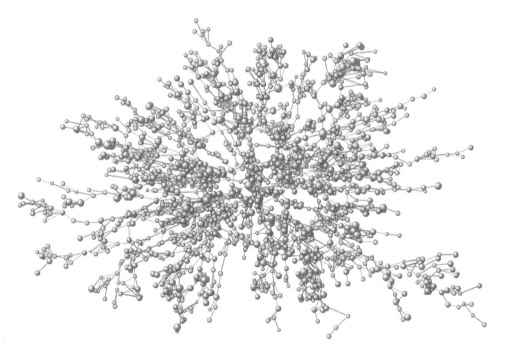

People copy each other: this social network graph shows the clustering of people of different body weights by their close relationships. The yellow bubbles represent people of heavy BMI and the green bubbles represent people of a low BMI. The red lines indicate close social ties between people. You can see that yellow bubbles are highly connected with each other, as are green bubbles, and there are less connections between the green and the yellow bubbles.

*Do less of this: image of what you **don't** want people to do.*

*Do more of this: image of what you **do** want people to do, that people can imitate.*

tributaries that transport your message to other people, to see how you can spread behaviors through the rivers of social interactions.

Here's how to get started—create posters that show an example of a person doing what you want everyone to do. Use language such as "everyone is doing it" or "81 percent of people are doing it." You can sponsor socially influential people in your community to adopt the behavior and exhibit it within their social networks. You can run a competition or campaign to get people to photograph themselves doing the behavior and post it on Instagram. You can hold parties where you talk about the issue and encourage people at your event to adopt the behavior at the party. Ask people in your movement not just to spread the message, but also to *display the behavior* to everyone they know.

Also, don't forget how powerful *your* individual actions can be. Each of your actions has a ripple effect that is bigger than the act itself. Your individual eco-friendly and pro-social behaviors are affecting everyone around you, and they are multiplying, even without you having to tell anyone about it. Every time you bring your reusable coffee cup to your local café, people are watching you, and copying you. When you install solar panels on your house and tell everyone at work about it, some of your co-workers may well do it too, even if it's a few years later. When your neighbors see you composting, they may well eventually compost, too. When your co-workers see you eating your plastic-free lunch day in and day out, they will copy you. Every time you do a publicly visible behavior, you are sending a powerful cultural ripple into the world that is affecting everyone who witnesses you, and you are probably making a much bigger change in the world than you realize.

I've seen how people react to my (sometimes weird) plant-based meals, time and time again. I don't call myself a vegan, and I don't push the way I eat onto anyone else. However, through the natural process of social diffusion, I've created many plant-based eaters along the way. Over the years, friends, roommates, family members, schoolmates, and co-workers have been curious about my giant sprouted salads and tofu ensembles. Without any requests or pushing by me, many of them just started to eat that way. Then randomly someone tells me in an excited voice, eager to share his breakthrough, *"Katie! I ordered a bean burrito for lunch today — all vegan!"* and I'm like, *"Yeah! Go you! That's fabulous!"* You might have a similar story yourself of seeing this kind of imitation play out in your own social groups. That's what it takes to change the world. Lots of behaviors, when copied by other people, all add up to make a cultural norm and when it gets big enough, it becomes a social revolution.

THE TIPPING POINT

People often want to know *"How do you get something to go mainstream quickly?"* The answer is, we don't. Similar to the process of social diffusion, all new technologies, products, and ideas spread through communities in a process called *The Technology Adoption Life-cycle.* It's also known as the *diffusion of innovation* curve. But not all good things we would like to happen in the world make it from their birth as a new idea all the way to becoming a mainstream norm.

So what is the difference between a new technology or behavioral practice (such as eating a vegan diet, or using a reusable coffee cup) that causes it to either remain trapped in the fringe cultures of Berkeley or Portland, or burgeon into a movement that spreads like wildfire? What does it take for a movement to take hold and be accepted and practiced by almost everyone? There's a special point in the Technology Adoption Life-cycle called *the tipping point.*(5) It's one point in the adoption of a new thing when the floodgates open and this thing very quickly spreads from being niche to being mainstream. Virus epidemics follow this pattern, as does the adoption of new phones and video games. It also happens for pro-environmental behaviors such as recycling, and for new kinds of environmental legislation such as mandatory plastic bag fees. It happens for moral value systems, such as it being normal to think that wearing fur or littering plastic is bad. All these practices that are now normal were once out of the norm. Then, one day, *the tipping point* was reached when *not* wearing fur and *not* littering turned from tiny fringe movements into mainstream cultural norms, endorsed by governments and celebrities around the world.

So what happened? The spread of all movements passes through five phases. Each of these phases can be characterized as the adoption of the movement by a specific *type* of person. Just as one domino pushes the next one over, the adoption of a new thing by one group of people encourages, or *enables,* the next group to join in. The groups, and the order they flow in, goes like this:

1st phase, *Innovators:* These are die-hard fans of a new thing who jump at the chance to be ahead of the pack and try new things. They make up 1 to 2.5 percent of the population.

2nd phase, *Early adopters:* These are people who want to be innovative, but prefer to jump into something new after they see a few people around them trying it first. They make up about 13.5 percent of the population.

3rd phase, *Early majority:* The early majority is the first large swathe of the population who will adopt something new once it has been well-proven by both the *innovators* and *early adopters.* They make up about 34 percent of the population.

4th phase, *Late majority:* These kinds of people simply don't want to be left out. They are essentially the *follower* type. They will jump on board only because they want to fit in with what the majority is already doing, and are not comfortable doing anything where they can't see at least 50 percent of people around them doing it. They make up about 34 percent of the population.

5th phase, *Laggards:* This group of people is pretty hard to get to do anything. They are unlikely to adopt anything new unless there are heavy penalties involved for not doing so. They make up about 16 percent of the population.

When you are changing the world, the thing you are promoting will initially be adopted only by a tiny group of people, the *innovators.* Once you've got a core following of *innovators* under wraps, the next group, the *early adopters* see them and think *"I wanna be like those cool people"* and so they buy your product or start doing the action you are promoting. This is the stage when the magical *tipping point* happens. Everything starts to snowball when you cross the 17 percent adoption line, and grow your movement from capturing the *early adopters* and break into the *third segment* that is the *early majority.* The *early majority* will think it seems pretty reasonable to jump on board once they see enough people around them doing it.

Once the *early majority* has jumped on, fifty percent of the population has joined your movement. At this point, the fourth group, the *late majority,* realize that they are now being left behind, and that they have actually become the *minority.* These people are natural followers and really do not like to be in the minority, so they jump on board, too. The last group are the *laggards* who you can never get to do anything. These are the people who *still* don't have an email

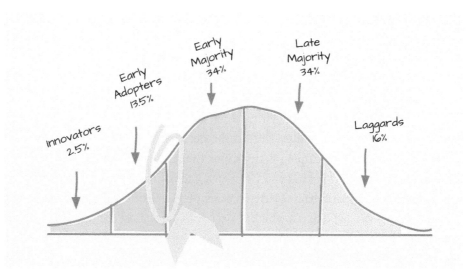

The Technology Adoption Life-cycle: five segments starting with a small group called the "innovators." Each segment enables the next portion of adoption to take hold. The tipping point occurs at a point between about 13 and 18 percent adoption, just before the early majority jump on board.

address or a smartphone, and have been eating the same thing for breakfast for 27 years with no plans to ever change. It's better to not exert much energy trying to convert these people to your movement.

A good example of an environmental movement that has recently crossed the tipping point is the banning or taxing of single-use plastic bags. In the 1990s, billions of plastic bags were freely and abundantly given out at cash registers all around the world. The bags were commonly littered on the street, bursting out of kitchen cupboards in every home, and often turning up in the stomachs of dead sea turtles and dolphins.

The practice of bringing reusable bags to the supermarket is now an everyday norm for most people in San Francisco where I live, but it was quite recently unheard of. I remember when I was fourteen years old, how excruciatingly intimidating it was to bring my own calico bag to Safeway. The behavior was so unusual back then that people would smirk and laugh at me in the checkout line. Anyone weird enough to bring her own cloth bag to the store had to brace for a potentially difficult, or at the very least awkward, interaction with the clerk at the register. It was a strange thing to do, and almost no one did it. Plastic bags were such an ordinary and common part of life for decades, that banning them was one of the last things that governments were interested in taking on.

It all started to change after the year 2000, and quickly. Many small community campaigns around the world had been pushing to end single-use plastic bags. The behavioral trend of people bringing their own reusable bags to the store, essentially boycotting the freely available disposable bags, had been growing. It has spread from just the *innovators* doing it, no matter how awkward it was, to the *early adopters* joining in too, and then it wasn't so weird anymore.

The movement got serious in 2002 when Bangladesh became the first country in the world to universally ban the bag. Then it snowballed. Through the 2000s, many countries and cities across Africa, Asia, Europe, and America started to ban the bag as well. All of a sudden, within the decade from 2005 to 2015, over 50 countries, from small developing nations like Tanzania and Myanmar, to wealthy developed countries like Ireland and Germany, had banned or enforced mandatory fees on single-use plastic bags.(6) After years of frustration from environmental groups and eco-minded citizens who had been pushing against the dominant norm, the tipping point was reached. The plastic bag went from being a daily norm to becoming maligned and scorned in only ten years, and it happened globally across every continent on Earth.

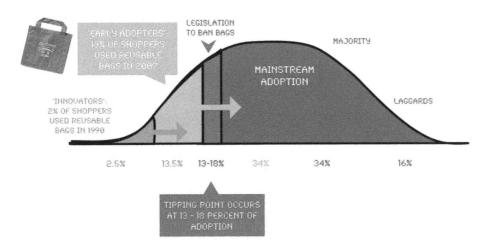

The tipping point of reusable bag adoption: change starts with 2 percent of shoppers, known as the "innovators," bringing reusable bags to the store. In 2007 in Australia, 13 percent of shoppers were bringing reusable bags. The tipping point occurs between 13 and 18 percent adoption, after which the government brought in legislation to ban free plastic bags.

What does it take to reach a tipping point? Tipping points are catalyzed from the efforts of two special types of people. The first kind is called a *social connector*. These type of people make friends easily, love to socialize frequently, and tend to know lots of people. Because all change happens through social networks, to make a tipping point happen, you need to have these social connector people telling all *their* social connections about it. They have the capacity to influence many people around them to engage with your movement.

The second type of person that helps build your tipping point is called an *innovator* or *maven*. These types are those who are experts in their fields and quite possibly in your movement, too. They are happy to be doing an unusual-cutting edge thing that not many other people are doing. They love to teach others what they know, and they love to learn. These people will bring credibility to your movement and will help to educate others around them about the intricacies of what your movement is about.(7)

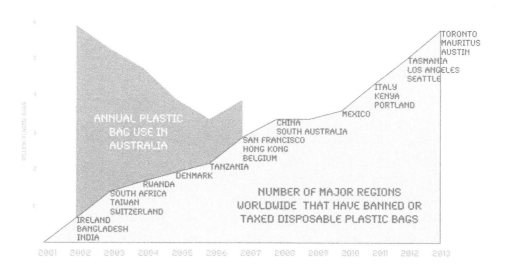

The rise of plastic bag bans through the 2000s. After the first plastic bags were banned in Bangladesh in 2002, many other counties and cities around the world followed, creating a global cascade of plastic bag bans.

BUILDING YOUR TRIBE

How do you get a network of *social connectors* and *mavens* to become so captivated by your campaign, product, or project, that they fall in love with it and tell everyone they know about it? There is no fancy marketing answer or psychological technique here. The answer is, that whatever it is you are building— *it needs to be great*. You don't need to think up something that lots of people will accept or react to with a shrug of lukewarm enthusiasm. You need to think up something that only a few people will absolutely and epically *fall in love* with. When you make something so powerful, compelling, and just so damn good, that it captures the hearts of a small number of these influential personality types, then you can enable your social connectors and mavens to do what they do best: to share, teach, and explore your movement, until it grows to reach its own tipping point.

There's a common and heart-breaking mistake that people all over the world make, every day, in the hope of being more liked. It's the flawed assumption that diluting your project's message, style, or look, to be more "mainstream" or easily "likable" will help it get accepted by more people. It's an illusion. Trying to be a little less unusual, a little less bold, or a little less controversial won't get you closer to *the tipping point* you need to reach to change the world. All you'll end up doing is not connecting with, and maybe even alienating, the very special social connectors and mavens who you need to become the self-appointed cheerleaders for your cause.

Everyone is hungry to be inspired. Everyone is yearning for meaning. *Social connectors* and *mavens*, just like everyone else, are craving things that are powerfully moving, ground-breaking, and novel. They want to discover things that *they* can share with the people whom *they* look up to, and the people *they* want to be adored by. There is no reason to wade around in the boring, vanilla, and politically correct "fitting in" version of what you do. It won't cut it. To reach the tipping point, your project needs to be *spectacular*. I promise you, there is a uniquely powerful story, look, and energy within the fabric of your cause that is itching to burst out. Your story *wants* to come to life in the most interesting, bright, and wildly captivating way possible, and turn into the spiritual food that people everywhere are craving.

Every so often a well-meaning person messages me on social media with feedback that one of my projects might "get out to more people" if I did x, y, or z to tone it down. Comments I've received have included, *"Maybe you should use less pink? It might turn off corporate clients, or confuse people, because you are really about being green,"* or *"If you added some meat to your vegan recipes, you'd*

> "Don't be trapped by dogma—which is living with the results of other people's thinking. Don't let the noise of other people's opinions drown out your own inner voice. And most important, have the courage to follow your own heart and intuition."
>
> — Steve Jobs

attract more people, because most of the world eats meat," and my favorite all-time regressive advice, *"If you didn't show your baby or flowers on your book cover, you'd get more men interested in buying your book, and it would get out to double the number of people."* (FYI plenty of men buy my zero waste book *Detrash Your Life in 90 Days,* even with a baby and flowers on the cover.) This type of advice always recommends that I remove parts of my work that make it unique and beautiful, and dilute my natural expression. But to what avail? So my projects become dull and uninteresting in the hope of getting out to more people? Building a movement just doesn't work that way.

We often wonder if *other people* will like what we make. But this kind of thinking commonly promoted in marketing and human-centered design tutorials, isn't always as smart as it sounds. Think about what happens when everyone in one community is perpetually checking in with everyone around them to see if they "like" what they are making. There's a risk that innovation can slide down a slippery slope into an echo-chamber, where everyone exists in a silo, reflecting the same ideas and visual style back to everyone else in the same silo. This doesn't mean we shouldn't ask for feedback and make our projects *likable*, but it does mean that other people's input isn't the *sole* compass guiding how we go about creating fabulous things that change the world.

Steve Jobs once said something that has always stuck with me. He said *"Don't be trapped by dogma—which is living with the results of other people's thinking. Don't let the noise of other's opinions drown out your own inner voice. And most important, have the courage to follow your own heart and intuition."* I interpreted his statement to mean that it doesn't matter if people around you like it. What matters is that *you* like it. If you

> ## "An individual artist needs only a thousand true fans in her tribe. It's enough."
>
> — Seth Godin, Tribes: We Need You to Lead Us

absolutely love what you're making, it doesn't matter. Then other people will like it too.

This idea has had a powerful effect on how I work. I stopped always wondering if *other people* like what I make. I threw the whole concept of a target customer, reader or key audience out of my head, and I stopped trying to design what I thought such a fictitious caricature would want to see. Instead, I started asking the question, *"Do *I like* what I'm making?"* The only thing I ask myself now is, *"Does this thing I made totally rock *my* world?"* I haven't looked back. If it doesn't pass my own personal standard of awesome, then it doesn't get out. If I can't fall in love with what I make, then how can I expect anyone else to?

Next time you have to make a decision on which way to lean, don't lean in the direction of being *more safe.* Be more weird. Be more wild. Be more crazy. Be more fun. Be more niche. Most of all, be *more interesting.* Don't worry too much about asking everyone else if they like what you are making. You don't need other people's permission to make your own work more authentically awesome.

But let's get back to building your movement. Start by getting *one hundred* people to become richly loyal fans of your cause. Ask yourself if your project is *good enough* to do that. Is it *good enough* for people to become obsessed about your cause and stay up late reading about it? Will they talk about it at their next dinner party like it's the coolest thing ever? Will they travel long distances to be a part of it? Would they send it to a potential love interest to reveal a feather-in-the-cap of the fascinating stuff they're into?

Once you can create this kind of passion in one hundred people, or even just *ten people*, you can then graduate to one thousand people. Seth Godin writes in his book *Tribes*, *"An individual artist needs only a thousand true fans in her tribe. It's enough."* If you can't get this kind of epic devotion from one hundred people, you won't be able to do it for one million—and those one million people won't be on board to tell their friends to grow your movement to ten million. This mindset of cultivating extreme love and devotion will force you to make your project, product, or campaign *truly exceptional*—so exceptional that it spreads rapidly from person to person, and can tip the culture of a whole generation.

STEP #9: TRIBES EXERCISE

1. Find your core tribe: Who are the core one hundred people who are going to love your cause no matter how unusual or fringe it might be? How are you going to get them to become your biggest fans? Make a list of your core fans. If you're just starting, start with ten people, then grow your fans to one hundred people.

2. Reach out to your evangelist community: Your evangelist community might be a little different than your core fans, because this group is made up of people who are socially active or have some kind of social influence or status. Who are the people who are going to tell as many people as possible about your cause? How are you going to get to know them?

3. Image of the action: Create an image or poster of a desirable or relatable person doing the action you want people to emulate.

4. Norms: Identify how you can use norms in your copy-writing, such as, "87 percent of people that came before you did this thing."

5. Support behaviors to mimic: How can you help your fans engage in behaviors that people around them will copy? How can you help them encourage others to copy them? How can you use images in your marketing showing what you want people to do in a way that they can imitate?

6. Empower sharing: What can you give your core fans that will encourage them to lead by example, or share knowledge with their family and friends? How are you going to empower your core evangelists to spread the word? Make a list of ideas of how you can support your fans to influence their friends, families, and co-workers.

7. Create mega-fans: How will you turn your fans into mega-fans? How can you create a strong and authentic bond with your fans that encourages them to grow from a regular fan into a *mega-fan*? This is the type of love that will get people talking and emphatically sharing their story with people around them. How can you upgrade your material to make it more awesome, more inspiring, in a way that will get people who like what you do to deeply fall in love with it? How are you going to encourage strong social bonds *between* your mega-fans?

STEP #10

TECHNOLOGY

"If I'd asked people what they wanted, they would have said 'faster horses.'"
— Attributed to Henry Ford

There's a reason that technology design is the final chapter in this book. It's because when tackling epic, planetary-wide challenges, like *saving the world* (for example), technology design should come *at the end* of a thorough research and design process. Not before, and not in-between. The technology you build needs to be a manifestation of a *really good* idea—and this idea should have taken considered thought, research, and testing. Think of technology development, not like an idea for an app, or some nerdy solution you magically pluck out of the air, but as the *wrapping* of all of the strategic ideas you've worked on in the preceding chapters of this book. Don't make the mistake that many people have made before you— jumping into writing code for a poorly thought-out concept that ends up floundering in the purgatory of the world's unused servers and abandoned Github repositories.

There's a neat metaphor I like to use to explain what I mean by *wrapping*. You know those little Russian dolls that have a doll inside another doll, inside another doll, with a tiny little doll in the middle? The concentric dolls illustrate how you can think about the layers of your social change strategy. Imagine that the tiny little doll in the very center represents your *data*. It's the core of your strategy, and all the other dolls exist to support it. The second Russian doll is the *behavior or action* you want your audience to do. The third doll is your *gamification & interface design,* such as color coding, star ratings, or leaderboards. Each doll represents a strategic layer that wraps around, and enables the next layer underneath to come to fruition.

Once you've figured out how these first three dolls—data, behaviors, and gamification design—are going to take shape, you've got a pretty good foundation for determining your project's technology needs. The fourth doll that wraps

Doll 1: Data - Measure the change in the data that is happening.
Doll 2: Behavior Change - Get people to do behaviors that affect the numbers.
Doll 3: Gamification - Enhance people's motivation to do a behavior.
Doll 4: Outreach - Grow the movement of people doing the behaviors.
Doll 5: Technology - Facilitate the whole process for many people to get involved and take action.

around all these dolls is *outreach*—all the marketing, education, and promotional strategies you'll use to draw people in and engage them with your project. The last Russian doll is *technology*. It comes last because, once you've got all these nested strategies fleshed out, you can look at the whole thing and think through how you can use technology to *enable* the whole system to reach its maximum potential.

The behavior map you did in Chapter Six will provide the skeleton for your technology design. Above all, your technology idea needs to answer the one fundamental question: *How can technology enable people in the real world, to make real behaviors, that move the numbers on your cause?* Remember from Chapter Five *"An idea is only a hypothesis."* Ask yourself if the technology you want to build will make change based on a reasonably provable *causal mechanism?* Take a bird's-eye view of your behavior map and look for areas where technology will be the most useful. How can you use technology to get people's attention to *engage* with your project? How can you use technology get them to *sign up to a pledge?* How can you use technology to enable people to *share* behaviors and ideas with their friends? How can you use technology to track people's *specific behavior changes or actions?* How can you use technology to *cue* people to act at the right point in time? How can you use technology to *gather data faster*, and *show that data* to people in real time? Looking at the whole system like this is a different way of developing technology than just randomly coming up with an idea for an app, or a widget, out of the context of your nest of Russian dolls and your map of behaviors that reveal what you want your target audience to do.

There's been an ethos in the startup world during the past few years that you must race to make an *MVP*—a "minimal viable product." If you haven't heard the term before, an MVP is the simplest skeleton version of your app that you can build and make live on the internet. It's not a terrible idea to rush into building an MVP. It gets startup teams out of the ideation phase and into the work phase. The founders can test their idea with real users, and prove to investors they have what it takes to actually create some technology that works.

But the risk of a quick MVP approach is that founders can dive into building an app before they take the time to understand the real-world problem their app or game is intended to solve. Living in Silicon Valley and being a part of the tech startup scene for at least ten years now, I see it happen all the time. A rush to MVP can be a recipe for many work-hours thrown away on bad ideas. All over the world, servers are littered with lines of code, dead startups, and app mockups that never turned into anything. While it's always good to make new things, I'm sure that you want a better destination for your social-change project.

Don't jump into building an MVP until you've *thoroughly researched* the real world data you want to change. Make sure you've embedded a system into your project *to measure the evidence* that your strategy is working. Don't write a single

When it comes to changing the world, an idea is only a *hypothesis*.

line of code until you've spent several hours on a behavior mapping exercise, and make sure your behavior map is *thorough and detailed*.

Behavior mapping is a critical process. It will provide the template of your app's user interface design and the blueprint of its functionality. Don't forget that the only purpose of any technology development you do is to drive people to *exhibit a certain behavior in the real world*—in the world that is *not* inside a computer. Your behavior map should show the journey your audience takes from the first step, when they engage with your technology, to the last step, where they come out of the app and do the *action*.

It's ok if it takes you a long time to study it first. The ecosystem of the problem you are working on is likely a thousand times more complex than the ecosystem that many consumer apps like *Pinterest*, *Guitar Tuner*, or *Candy Crush* exist in. There's no need to rush into "building something," when haste might cause you to actually build a bad idea. Cheap apps that can be built quickly can also die quickly. Solving some of the world's most difficult problems takes time, and that's ok.

The world is dripping with opportunities for technology that can help us solve many of our greatest planetary challenges. In the last decade, building blocks and components you can use to make new technology products have taken an exponential leap. You can now get Arduino micro-controllers, mapping apps, software libraries, sensors, cloud servers and just about everything else you might need easily and quite inexpensively on the internet. All you need to do is put the parts together, not unlike a set of Legos. Heck, you can even buy a DIY gene editing kit called a CRISPR from my friend Josiah in Oakland, California for under $100. He used it to make a bacteria that literally eats and decomposes plastic pollution. You know what else is crazy? In 2018 it became possible to buy a small DIY satellite kit and launch your own satellite into space for about $10,000— including the rocket-ship ticket and all. These are all very new developments. Advanced technology tools are becoming accessible to everyone, and it's changing everything.

The reason I've used the word "technology" in this chapter more and the word "app" less is because I want you to break free from the cult of app or platform development and try and think *outside* the screen. Don't let your imagination be confined to iPhone screens and laptops. The world is a canvas for your technology design. You can use all kinds of lights, touch screens, and sensors outside of the conventional app.

It doesn't even need to be electronic. Here's the thing about low-tech—it's easy. Much can be achieved with a cardboard sign on the door reminding you to bring your reusable bags to the store. Signs, stickers, and refill stations are all examples of effective low-tech solutions that can often work better than something complicated on a computer. Whichever end of the spectrum—from technophilic to technophobic—you find yourself on, it's good to explore both ends a bit more. Your magical solution that changes the world might just be a blend of cardboard and silicon.

Don't get sucked into the dualistic idea that *some* people are engineers who are good with technology, while *others* are just bad at it. The only difference is that some people have invested more hours to learn it. Don't be afraid of rolling up your sleeves and taking an online coding course and embracing the challenges and wonders of technology. You'd be surprised how much you can learn and what you can do when you put your mind to it. Make something that no one has ever made before, and go change the world with it.

Don't write a single line of code until you've spent several hours on a detailed *behavior map*. It will provide the template of your app design.

TECHNOLOGY COMPONENTS & IDEAS

Here are some ideas for how you can use electronic components and software to create technology that can help you change the world.

✦ Connect color LED lights to air quality or water quality sensors using an Arduino or Raspberry Pi.

✦ Get high-resolution satellite imagery to help survey forest cover, glacier size, erosion, or mining activity that is refreshed almost daily from planet.com or eos.com.

✦ Convert satellite or aerial images to data arrays. You can do this by using Python code libraries to break the image up into pixels, storing the information contained in each pixel as a data point in an array. You can write algorithms that detect the size of coal mines, track fishing or whaling boats, or compute percentage of urban tree cover.

✦ Use drones and sensors to monitor endangered species.

✦ Use Google Earth Engine to process data in maps and make visualizations.

✦ Show data, color, or cues to get people to act, using small screen displays such as the Raspberry Pi 7" touch screen.

✦ Create large public screen displays (available from dell.com) that render your data in commercial locations.

✦ Purchase environmental sensors on sparkfun.com, amazon.com, or libelium.com to measure what you want to change.

✦ Use thermal cameras from FLIR to see energy leaks or hot spots in buildings or factories.

✦ Mockup a realistic looking prototype of your app idea using hotgloo.io or figma.com.

✦ Visually represent your data on map apps using mapbox.com or Google Maps.

✦ Learn how to visualize your data using a javascript library like d3js.org.

✦ Get familiar with putting your data into a database like Mysql or MongoDB. If you're not ready for a database, start by putting your data in a spreadsheet like Microsoft Excel or Google Spreadsheets.

✦ Create an electronic billboard that shows data visualizations.

✦ Install a sensor by your front door that beeps if you forget your re-usable water bottle.

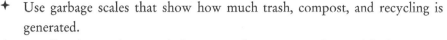

- Use garbage scales that show how much trash, compost, and recycling is generated.
- Install a device that regularly reports how many gallons of fuel your car uses.
- Design a better smart meter energy display for homes that shows the data in color.
- Bring environmental footprint data and carbon accounting into consumer barcodes.
- Use mailgun.com for sending automatic email notifications to members, with custom data.
- Start learning from sites like teamtreehouse.com, lynda.com, codeacademy.com, codeschool.com, hackster.io, instructables.com, or khanacademy.org.

Need help?
- Look through upwork.com to find freelance designers and computer programmers to help you build your idea.

Marketing and web technology

- Build an email signup system or create an email learning course using mailchimp.com, convertkit.com, or ontraport.com.
- Make videos using imovie or Adobe Premier Pro and upload them to YouTube.
- Do your own graphic design with canva.com.
- Join the Adobe Creative suite for about $50 per month to get access to professional-grade creative tools. Every Adobe product is learnable with a few hours of watching video tutorials.
- Build websites in a few minutes using wordpress.com or easy web-builders like squarespace.com, weebly.com, or wix.com.
- Use shopping site-builders like shopify.com to sell items, Gumroad to sell digital products, or Patreon to gathering monthly contributions.
- Use online recurring billing systems like Paypal and Recurly, Stripe, or Chargify.
- Use Hootsuite.com or MeetEdgar.com to schedule social media posts on rotation.

STEP #10: TECHNOLOGY CHECKLIST

1. Review your behavior map: Look through your behavior map from Chapter Six and think through how you can use technology to help people do more of the behaviors you want them to do.

2. Low-tech options: Think through all the low-tech solutions, (such as using printed signs, stickers, or altering the physical environment) you can apply to this problem before trying to build new technology.

3. Data in a database: Put your data in a database such as MySQL, or MongoDB, that can be queried by another computer.

4. Feedback loop: Think through how you can build a feedback loop of your real-world measurements into your technology design. This means that you are measuring what you want to change, showing these numbers to people, updating the data as frequently as possible, and prompting people to make a change in the real world.

5. Russian dolls: Look through the Russian dolls approach to technology and consider how you've designed your technology to connect the data through to the user in a feedback loop with these layers.

6. Front-end display of data: Display your data on a front-end device such as web browser or touch screen. Use data visualizations libraries such as d3js.org.

7. Test and iterate: Test and iterate your design using a lean and agile method. Do a tiny bit of work on your product, then test it with people, gather feedback, make some changes, then test it again. Don't code too much before testing it on people and getting feedback from them.

Beware of doing this

➢ Beware of jumping into a technology design without doing a detailed behavior mapping exercise. You need to be specific about the action you want the user to take, and to make sure the technology guides the user toward doing this real-world action.

➢ Don't design technology that doesn't put the real-world numbers at the core of the design.

➢ Remember that building an app, website, or technology product in itself probably won't make change happen. Clicks, downloads, and users aren't real-world change. It's in the actions that *human beings* take in the real world, not on the computer, that the change occurs.

➢ Don't underestimate yourself. You can make big technology leaps on your own simply by looking up how to do it on Google and asking people around you for help. There are online tutorials for just about anything you might ever want to build. Use websites like teamtreehouse.com, lynda.com, codeschool.com, instructables.com, and hackster.io to keep learning.

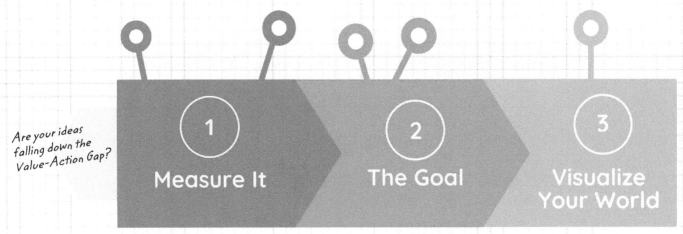

1.1 Determine your "God" metric that defines your issue in real-world physical matter.

1.2 What does the data say about where your issue is now?

2.1 Determine your goal metric that makes your problem "solved."

2.2 Write your quantitative mission statement.

3.1 Visualize your future world and draw it.

Are your ideas falling down the Value-Action Gap?

1 Measure It

2 The Goal

3 Visualize Your World

How to Save the World

in Summary

Take action! Do the things it takes to bring your ideas to life.

10 Technology

9 Tribes & Tipping Points

8b Tell Your Story

Believe in your own creative potential and invest 1 hr per day in your creative genius zone.

10.2 Design your technology to get real humans to make changes in the real world.

10.1 Collect your data in granular detail, and in real time.

9.3 Build a community of 100 super fans.

9.2 Make your branding unique to what rocks *your* world.

9.1 Display the actions you want people to imitate.

8b.1 Use *The Hero's Journey* to tell your story with your audience as the hero.

8a.6 Design a novel and fun experience for your player.

4.1 Harvest 100 ideas from your visualization that will get us from the current world to this future world.

6.1 Identify your actor, action and result.

4
Idea Storm

5
Idea Evaluation

6.2 De-cluster your target behavior into specific sub-behaviors.

Follow the ten steps along the rainbow to turn your dreams for a better world into an idea, project, startup, or campaign that doesn't just talk about change, but makes real and measurable change happen in the world every day.

6.3 Do a behavior/user story mapping exercise.

6
Behavior Change

6.4 Ask people to write down a pledge to do the target behavior.

6.5 Use *Foot in the Door Technique* to ask people for tiny commitments.

8a
Game Design

7
Systems Thinking

6.6 Include social norms in your copy-writing.

8a.1 Build a feedback loop of the data you are trying to affect.

8a.4 Give awards and badges.

8a.3 Create a progress bar with your goal data.

8a.2 Rank your players with comparisons and leaderboards.

8a.5 Apply star ratings and color grades.

Thanks for the idea for this chart, Chris!

IT'S THE END, BUT IT'S REALLY THE BEGINNING

"One can have no smaller or greater mastery than mastery of oneself."
— Leonardo da Vinci

There's one thing I've noticed from giving workshops and talks about the ten steps in this book: everyone loves to *learn* about them. People come up with wonderful ideas and send me heart-lifting emails about how much they enjoyed learning all the techniques. But there's a gap—and that's the gap of *doing* it.

This is the gap that exists between the wonderful idea in your mind, and the humble, vulnerable, and imperfect steps you will need to take to make your idea come true in real life. Some change-makers cross this moat nearly every day in order to change the world. Yet other aspiring world-changers sit at the precipice, circling their ideas, and hold back from giving it all they've got. Why do so many people who feel big passion to change the world hold back on implementing their ideas? How do we *all* get better at jumping over the crevasse of our own possible inaction every day?

The early phase of any world-changing concept is always fun. It involves learning, thinking, dreaming, and ideating—it's fun because it's still only a *fantasy*. Turning a beautiful fantasy in your mind into a *real* project that makes *real* change on the ground might well be one of the hardest things a human being can do. It will make you confront your own emotional limitations, solve brain-breaking difficult technical challenges, and take on intimidating powerful industries. Sometimes the biggest enemy isn't all the plastic in the ocean. Sometimes the biggest enemy is inaction, and overcoming it requires taking a single step in a single hour: a humble, vulnerable, and imperfect step, across the tiny unglamorous gap in front of you, that is the bravest thing of all.

Pursue Your Own Mastery

We can't get real about saving the world without addressing our individual quest for purpose and meaning. There's an inextricable connection between the pursuit of happiness, the craving to fulfill our potential, and the desire each of us has to change the world. There's a thread that draws all of it together, and it has the power to pull each of us off our perch of sitting on the edge, and into the flow of *making ideas happen*. This thread is the craftsmanship and *pursuit of mastery* of our own unique calling. There's an intrinsically natural motivation to always improve one's own skills and gifts, and when you get in the flow of living it daily, it is more powerful than the call of any to-do list, activist agenda, or even the obligation to simply turn up to a regular job each day.

We make small choices every day about which side of our own mastery to walk on. We can choose the side where we hold back, or the other side we dig deeper. These choices are all around us. It's in the big things, like leaving a corporate job to start the NGO of your dreams, or enrolling in a Ph.D. program, but mostly, it's in the little things. It's learning to write code, instead of holding back and living in fear of your first HTML tag. It's spending a weekend studying Photoshop tutorials when you never thought you could draw, let alone be good at using a computer. It's re-writing your TEDx talk for the eleventh time and reaching for some other-worldly force to get it from *good* to *standing ovation phenomenal*. It's in finding every opportunity in all the minutes of all the days to technically, creatively, and spiritually push against the limits of what you think you are capable of and confronting the awkward frustration that comes over you when you push into the unchartered territory of your creative growth. Experiencing life through the lens of creative mastery is like holding a magnifying glass up to the world and seeing a deeper layer of complexity, beauty, and curiosity in all things.

You live it through the continual mindfulness and intention to deliberately put your inner wellspring of energy behind your own creative focus. It's this energy that weaves together the big drivers of the soul: our quest for meaning, purpose, happiness, and to fulfill our own potential. Sometimes it's effortless. Sometimes it's hard. The grind is in the creative process, and when you get this right, God takes care of the rest.

In Creative Challenge You Are Forged

Just as world-changing technical and creative projects can gush with inspiration and joy, they usually come with equal portions of suffering. It's a unique kind of pain that we should embrace and feel more deeply. It's not the usual kind of pain that comes from something like a sick family member, a break-up, a dismal house, or whatever unfortunate circumstance might befall you. It's a very specific kind of anxiety that comes when we venture to the outer edge of our capacity to do great work. It's that zone that pulls your neurons in awkwardly weird and unusual ways when you embark on new and difficult things, like re-working your website into a visual work of art or re-imagining your startup's vision into gobsmackingly awe-inspiring. It's the exertion it takes to lovingly sculpt each little phrase in your prose, like a sculptor smooths over clay, or an athlete pushes through the pain of another lap, or a mother pushes deeper into unfathomable fatigue that comes with caring for a new baby. You know you're in the zone when you're saying things like "*I have no fucking idea what I am doing . . . This is the hardest thing I've ever done . . . If you told me two years ago I would be doing this, I would have said you are crazy . . . This is my dream job/project . . . I just got so fascinated and obsessed by it I couldn't *not* do it.*"

There is an inextricable interdependence between inspiration and suffering. Justine Musk gave a TED talk where she summed up the musings of important people like Jesus, Einstein, and Joseph Campbell into this, "*Pursue your own bliss, not because it will lead you to a blissful life. But because if you connect those moments of authentic happiness, they will lead you to something much bigger than what makes you happy—which is something that you are willing to suffer for.*" Bliss and suffering are bound to each other. When you push into projects you haven't done, and talents you have not practiced, you'll get crushed, scraped and

This is the process of the universe carving you into shape, and this shape is unique to you. It's your creative genius zone in the making, and it can't be replicated by anyone else.

squished. Many people feel deterred by this phase. Don't be. It's in those moments of creatively pushing yourself for what you believe in, that you forge something new inside you, something that wasn't there before. Like a piece of clay being torn and reformed, or a rod of steel being beaten into shape, you stretch and mold into something stronger and smarter than before. This is the process of the universe carving you into shape, and this shape is *unique to you*. It's your creative genius zone in the making, and it can't be replicated by anyone else.

We find our truth in that layer between excruciating suffering and break-through. We are fascinated by the story of overcoming difficulty, of forging new skills, and discovering new worlds. We do it in the Olympics. We make movies about it. We have Guinness World Records about it. We are made for the pain of doing difficult things, and the joy of breaking through. It hurts, but somehow there is a fierceness that comes with venturing boldly into the wild of a mission you are yet to master. When you venture into the wild of the most confronting corners of your ideas and of your abilities, you come out of it with the wild in you.

What will you find on the other side of your creative breakthrough? What new people will you meet as a result of posting your first YouTube video, even if it's not *that* good? What insight will you get from another batch of petri dish experiments that have already failed 29 times? What funding could you be provided when you make that intimidating phone call to kickstart your idea? There is nothing to be afraid of. All we can do is be in the game. Theodore Roosevelt once said, *"The credit belongs to the man who is actually in the arena, whose face is marred by dust and sweat and blood; who strives valiantly; who errs, who comes short again and again; who knows great enthusiasms, the great devotions; who spends himself in a worthy cause; who at the best knows in the end the triumph of high achievement, and who at the worst, if he fails, at least fails while daring greatly."* What matters is being in the arena. When you are committed to creative expression, there is no failure. There are only drafts.

The world's evolution happens in the zone between your moments of inspiration and when you stretch your skills like you never thought possible. This is the zone where the magic is.

Happiness is Harvested from the Cycle

Even though the job of changing the world is often filled with a feeling of purpose and exuberance, it isn't a stairway to the elusive plateau of happiness, and it's not meant to be. The deep motivations for why we get involved in a social-change project can easily pull to the very core our soul, and illicit our most dramatic existential yearning. So why do it?

Happiness can be hard to achieve. You can't write a list of all the things that make you happy, like eating ice cream and walking in the park, then go do more of them, and suddenly experience the sense of place, purpose, love, usefulness, and community that are core to the human's search for meaning. There's something more substantial at work in the human experience than the pursuit of happiness.

The Hero's Journey story format lives through the ages because it reflects the core human experience, where life is made up of endless quests. We are called to take on a new challenge, leap into the void of uncertainty, then train, grow, and experience the suffering that comes when we stretch ourselves. Then out of the cauldron of our own creative growth, we create something beautiful. We come out the other side transformed, and in some of these moments, we experience happiness. Happiness is not a plateau we hike to reach. It's a cycle. Moments of true happiness and bliss are then discovered along the way, in bites of experiences, like finding strawberries in a field. Happiness is *harvested* like a fruit from the creative process of cultivating and then contributing our gift to the world.

A Tool that Channels the Force

There's a fascinating trend that comes up amongst great creative people in history that I think is reflective of the spiritual nature of changing the world. It's common for these people to refer to themselves as a vehicle, or a tool, through which they channel a creative energy—and curiously, don't feel all that personally responsible for it.

The famous futurist, inventor, and architect, Bucky Fuller, had a string of bad life events in his early life and experienced such severe depression that he had become suicidal. One night when he was looking into Lake Michigan, ready to drown himself, a voice said to him, *"You do not belong to you. You belong to the universe. Your significance will remain forever obscure to you, but you may assume that you are fulfilling your role if you apply yourself to converting your experiences to the highest advantage of others."* He ultimately chose to embark on what he called *"An experiment, to find what a single individual could contribute to changing the world and benefiting all humanity."*(1) Since that moment, Bucky

Moments of true happiness and bliss are *harvested* from the creative process of cultivating our gift, and then contributing its fruits to the world.

Fuller published over 30 books, worked as a professor of art and design, received prestigious design awards from around the world, and remained married to the love of his life for 66 years until they both passed away, from different causes, within 11 days of each other.

It seems that we discover our highest purpose when we put ourselves to work as a tool that channels creative energy in a way that does the most good in the world. It takes us out of the relentless pursuit of achievement, and defines us not by a salary, who we're connected to, but into another dimension that is defined by the quality of what we *contribute*. There really is no joy quite like making the world a better place every day, and doing it in a way that feels truly creatively authentic.

The Latent Force Breaks Through

The mastery of your inner creative force is the greatest contribution you can make to the world. The future is made of lots of people, people like you, taking lots of little leaps. All these little leaps add up. A phone call leads to an introduction that leads to a grant. An online tutorial leads to a blog that leads to the creation of a useful new software platform. A dinner meetup with friends leads to a conference which leads to a campaign that changes a law. They add up to a breakthrough, and when one person makes a breakthrough, the breakthrough ripples through the world for everyone to share. Don't forget Margaret Mead's famous quote, *"Never doubt that a small group of thoughtful, committed citizens can change the world; indeed, it's the only thing that ever has."* Sometimes they are big, like Einstein's E=mc2, and sometimes they are smaller, like helping a class of girls graduate high school, but each plays its role. Your breakthroughs are a contribution to the Earth and all to of humankind.

Sometimes I get this feeling that there is this enormous latent energy in humanity just waiting to break forth. I think of all the people who are craving more meaning in their work and who are on the cusp of their next breakthrough—

the engineers who are slashing technical boundaries, the entrepreneurs hunting for their next idea, and the culminating zeitgeist of everyone's intention to do better. I wonder what would happen if everyone started pushing into their creative genius intently, for just one hour a day, and contributed it to what they most care about. I look at all the incredible things humans have done, and keep doing, and wonder what more we are truly and ultimately capable of.

A Beautiful Future

I can see a future world where the era of humans harming the Earth has come to a close, and we become the custodians of our planet—a world in which technology, human civilization, and nature work together in ecological symbiosis. I can see a future where we have learned to elegantly maintain our biosphere and our society through delicate measurement of the Earth's systems and self-regulating feedback systems of data. We develop technology in partnership with nature, not at the expense of it.

The only limiting factor in saving the world is the ferocity with which we put our creative energy to work. Don't ever stop following your imagination. Follow the thread of curiosity. It's your road map, not only to your own future, but also to the collective future of our world.

HOW YOU CAN HELP SUPPORT
HOW TO SAVE THE WORLD

 **PATREON**

Contribute a monthly donation to the *How to Save the World* podcast and get special rewards at patreon.com/katiepatrick.

 **UDEMY**

Keep learning and enroll in my online course *Save the World with Design, Data Viz, and Gamification* at udemy.com/save-the-world-with-gamification.

 **AMAZON**

Did you love this book? Let others know about it and write a review on Amazon.com.

 **YOUTUBE**

Subscribe to the *How to Save the World* Youtube channel at youtube.com/c/HowtoSavetheWorld.

 **ITUNES**

Listen to the *How to Save the World* podcast on iTunes.com, subscribe, and leave a review.

GOT FEEDBACK, THOUGHTS, NEW IDEAS, OR A STORY FOR VERSION 2.0 OF HOW TO SAVE THE WORLD?

Do you want to contribute to the next edition of *How to Save the World?* I'll be releasing updated versions of the book periodically with new case studies and improvements. Email your thoughts, suggestions, or insights to kjs@helloworld.com

If you loved this book, let me know! Send me a couple of sentences about how it affected you or any ideas that came to mind while doing the exercises.

I'd love to hear from you.

RECOMMENDED READING

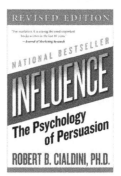

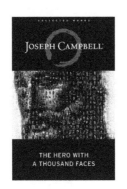

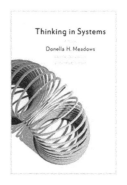

HELLO WORLD LABS CREATIONS

Email Katie at kp@helloworlde.com or sign up to helloworlde.com to learn more about these products or about having designs or concepts made for you that use environmental data to catalyze change.

262

References

Introduction

1. Kollmuss & Agyeman (2002). *Mind the Gap: Why do people act environmentally and what are the barriers to pro-environmental behavior?* Environmental Education Research.

2. Kowalska-Pyzalska, Maciejowska, Suszczyński, Sznajd-Weron, Weron (2014). *Turning green: Agent-based modeling of the adoption of dynamic electricity tariffs.* Energy Policy | Gadenne, Sharma, Kerr, Smith (2011). *The influence of consumers' environmental beliefs and attitudes on energy saving behaviours.* Energy Policy.

3. Chatzidakis, Hibbert (2007). Why People Don't Take their Concerns about Fair Trade to the Supermarket: The Role of Neutralisation. *Journal of Business Ethics.*

4. Boulstridge, Carrigan (2000). *Do consumers really care about corporate responsibility? Highlighting the attitude—behaviour gap,* Journal of Communication Management.

5. World Bank. CO2 emissions (metric tons per capita), Carbon Dioxide Information Analysis Center, Environmental Sciences Division.

How I Got Here

1. Wikipedia, *Mururoa French Nuclear Testing,* en.wikipedia.org/wiki/Moruroa.

2. Wikipedia, *Battery Cage,* en.wikipedia.org/wiki/Battery_cage.

3. Ballinger. *Nike Chronology,* Center for Communication & Civic Engagement, depts.washington.edu/ccce/polcommcampaigns/NikeChronology.htm

4. International Crisis Group (2007). *Nigeria - Ending the unrest in the Niger Delta.*

5. Armstrong & Roach (1997). *McLibel: Two People Who Wouldn't Say Sorry, Spanner Films, London.*

6. Wikipedia, *Rwandan Civil War,* en.wikipedia.org/wiki/Rwandan_Civil_War.

7. Kirby, Laurance, Albernaz, Schroth, Fearnside, Bergen, Venticinque, Costa, Carlos (2006). *The future of deforestation in the Brazilian Amazon.* Futures.

8. Ross & Isaac (2004). *The net effect: A review of cetacean bycatch in pelagic trawls and other fisheries in the north-east Atlantic,* A WDCS report for Greenpeace.

Chapter 1: Measure it

1. Fung, Rourke (2000). *Reinventing Environmental Regulation from the Grassroots Up: Explaining and Expanding the Success of the Toxics Release Inventory,* Harvard University, Environmental Management.

2. US Environmental Protection Agency (2018). *Light-Duty Automotive Technology, Carbon Dioxide Emissions, and Fuel Economy Trends: 1975 Through 2017.*

3. Fung, Graham, Weil (2008). *Full Disclosure: The Perils and Promise of Transparency,* Cambridge University Press, Boston.

4. Zhe Jin & Leslie (2003). The Effect of Information on Product Quality: Evidence from Restaurant Hygiene Grade Cards, *The Quarterly Journal of Economics.*

5. Australian Energy Rating Scheme energyrating.gov/about.

6. Tuppen (2008). *The carbon chasm - based on carbon disclosure project 2008 responses from the world's 100 largest companies,* The Carbon Disclosure Project, United Kingdom.

7. Faruqui, Sergici & Sharif (2010). *The impact of informational feedback on energy consumption: A survey of the experimental evidence,* Energy: The International Journal.

8. Allcott & Rogers (2014). *The Short-Run and Long-Run Effects of Behavioral Interventions: Experimental Evidence from Energy Conservation,* American Economic Review.

9. Loewenstein, Sunstein & Golman (2014). *Disclosure: Psychology Changes Everything,* Annual Review of Economics.

Chapter 3: Visualize Your World

1. Mollen, Saar, Ruiter, Robert, Kok, Gerjo (2010). *Current issues and new directions in Psychology and Health: What are the oughts? The adverse effects of using social norms in health communication,* Psychology & Health.

2. Kaufman, Gregoire (2016). Wired to Create, TarcherPerigee.

3. Garfield (1985). *Peak Performance: Mental Training Techniques of the World's Greatest Athletes,* Grand Central Publishing.

4. Sharot (2011). *The Optimism Bias,* Current Biology.

5. Hernandez (2015). *Optimism and Cardiovascular Health: Multi-Ethnic Study of Atherosclerosis,* Health Behavior and Policy Review.

6. Amabile, Kramer (2011). *The Progress Principle: Using Small Wins to Ignite Joy, Engagement, and*

Creativity at Work. Harvard Business Review Press.

7. Sapolsky (1992). *Stress, the Aging Brain, and the Mechanisms of Neuron Death.* The MIT Press.

8. Ansell (2012). *Cumulative Adversity and Smaller Grey Matter Volume in Medial Prefrontal, Anterior Cingulate, and Insula Regions.* Biological Psychiatry.

9. Corbetta, Shulman (2002). Control of goal-directed and stimulus-driven attention in the brain. *National Review of Neuroscience.*

10. Garrison (2015). *Meditation leads to reduced default mode network activity beyond an active task,* Cognitive, Affective, & Behavioral Neuroscience.

11. Beaty (2017). *Robust Prediction of Individual Creative Ability from Brain Functional Connectivity.* Proceedings of the National Academy of Sciences.

Chapter 6: Behavior Change

1. Freedman & Fraser (1966). *Compliance without pressure: The foot-in-the-door technique",* Journal of Personality and Social Psychology.

2. Mckenzie-Mohr (2001). *Turn it off: reducing vehicle engine idling final report,* Natural Resources Canada.

3. Dupré (2014). *The comparative effectiveness of persuasion, commitment and leader block strategies in motivating sorting,* Waste Management.

4. Bachman & Katzev (1982). *The effects of non-contingent free bus tickets and personal commitment on urban bus ridership.* Transportation Research

5. Lokhorst, Werner, Staats, Dijk & Gale (2013). *Commitment and Behavior Change: A Meta-Analysis and Critical Review of Commitment-Making Strategies in Environmental Research,* Environment and Behavior

6. Homonoff (2017). *Scientific support for a plastic bag reduction law,* New York University, Scientist Action and Advocacy Network.

7. Eliasson (2014). *The Stockholm congestion charges: an overview,* Center for Transport Studies, KTH Royal Institute of Technology.

8. Gneezy & Rustichini (2000). *A fine is a price. The University of Chicago,* Journal of Legal Studies.

9. Xiaojing, Arpan, Laura, Chen, Chien-fei (2015). *The Moderating Role of Individual Differences in Responses to Benefit and Temporal Framing of Messages Promoting Residential Energy Saving,* Journal of Environmental Psychology.

10. Dogan, Bolderdijk, Steg (2014). *Making small numbers count: environmental and financial feedback in promoting eco-driving behaviours,* Journal of Consumer Policy.

11. Krukow (2013). *Design to nudge and change behaviour: Sille Krukow at TEDxCopenhagen,* TEDx.

12. Rosen (2014). *Energy saving: Deena Rosen at TEDxUtrecht,* TEDx.

13. Irwin (2013). *If you want to motivate someone, shut up already,* Harvard Business Review.

14. Sparkman & Walton (2017). *Dynamic norms promote sustainable behavior, even if it is counternormative,* Stanford University, Psychological Science.

Chapter 7: Systems Thinking

1. Institute For Criminal Policy Research (2016). *The World Prison Brief,* University of London.

2. *McLaughlin, Pettus-Davis, Brown, Veeh, Renn (2016). The Economic Burden of Incarceration in the US,* Concordance Institute for Advancing Social Justice, Washington University.

3. Wikipedia.org/wiki/United_States_Environmental_Protection_Agency

4. Wikipedia.org/wiki/NASA.

5. Kelly (2015). *Criminal Justice at the Crossroads: Transforming Crime and Punishment,* Columbia University Press.

6. Cormack, Lawrence, Morrissette, Silver (2009). *If You Want to Change Violence in the 'Hood, You Have to Change the 'Hood: Violence and Street Gangs in Winnipeg's Inner City,* Canadian Centre for Policy Alternatives.

7. *Davidai, Gilovich, Ross (2012). The meaning of default options for potential organ donors.* Proceedings of the National Academy of Sciences.

Chapter 8a: Game Design

1. Teague Labs (2010). *DIY Arduino water meter.* labs.teague.com/?p=722

2. Darby (2001). *Making it obvious: Designing feedback into energy consumption.*

3. Katzev & Mishima (1992). *The use of posted feedback to promote recycling.* Psychological Reports.

4. Larson, Houlihan, & Goernert (1995). *Brief report: Effects of informational feedback on aluminum can recycling.* Behavioral Interventions.

5. Goetz (2011). *Harnessing the power of feedback loops,* Wired Magazine.

6. Steg & Vlek (2008). *Encouraging pro-environmental behaviour: An integrative review and research agenda,* Journal of Environmental Psychology.

7. US Energy Information Association (2009). Residential Energy Consumption Survey RECS.

8. US Energy Information Association (2018). eia.gov FAQ.

9. U.S. Statistics (2000) AF&PA | Pulp and Paper International (2014).

10. World Bank (2014). CO_2 emissions (metric tons per capita) data.worldbank.org

11. US Environmental Protection Agency (2014). *Pesticides Industry Sales and Usage 2008 – 2012 Market Estimates.*

12. USA Environmental Protection Agency (2013). *Advancing Sustainable Materials Management: Facts and Figures 2013.*

13. National Oceanic & Atmospheric Administration (2018). Trends in Atmospheric Carbon Dioxide, esrl.noaa.gov/gmd/ccgg/trends

14. Cuddy, Doherty, & Bos (2010). *Opower: Increasing Energy Efficiency through Normative Influence,* Harvard Business Review Case Study.

15. USA Environmental Protection Agency (2018). *Inventory of US greenhouse gas emissions & sinks 1990 - 2016.*

16. Patrick (2017). *How big water is getting you to change,* How to Save the World Podcast, Itunes.

17. Benedicto Klich (2014). *Leadership Lessons from the Mayor Who Put an Obese City on a Diet,* Entrepreneur Magazine. | thiscityisgoingonadiet.com | Cornett (2013). How an obese town lost a million pounds, TEDMED.

18. Landers & Landers (2015). *An Empirical Test of the Theory of Gamified Learning - The Effect of Leaderboards on Time-on-Task and Academic Performance,* Old Dominion University, Simulation & Gaming.

19. Holt-Lunstad & Smith (2010). *Social Relationships and Mortality Risk: A Meta-analytic Review,* Brigham Young University, PLOS Medicine.

20. Thompson (2007). *Desktop orb could reform energy hogs.* Wired Magazine.

21. USA Environmental Protection Agency (2013). *Advancing Sustainable Materials Management: Facts and Figures 2013.*

22. Fung, Graham, Weil (2008). *Full Disclosure: The Perils and Promise of Transparency,* Cambridge University Press, Boston.

23. Neighbors Against Irresponsible Logging (NAIL) Google Earth, Rebecca Moore google.com/earth/outreach/success-stories/neighbors-against-irresponsible-logging-nail

24. Columbia University, *New York City Building Energy Map* qsel.columbia.edu/nycenergy/about.html

25. Global Fishing Watch globalfishingwatch.org/map

26. MIT Senseable Cities Lab, *MIT Trash Track* senseable.mit.edu/trashtrack

27. Berkeley Labs, *Roof Albedo Map* albedomap.lbl.gov

28. Gallus (2016). *Fostering Voluntary Contributions to a Public Good: A Large-Scale Natural Field Experiment at Wikipedia,* Management Science, Forthcoming.

29. Kidwell, Lazarević, Baranski, Hardwicke, Piechowski, & Falkenberg (2016). *Badges to Acknowledge Open Practices: A Simple, Low-Cost, Effective Method for Increasing Transparency,* Journal of Psychological Science.

30. Kraut (1973). *Effects of social labeling on giving to charity.* Journal of Experimental Social Psychology.

31. Maldonado & Nass (2005). *Emotive characters can make learning more productive and enjoyable,* Stanford University, Journal of Educational Technology.

32. Wikipedia. UC Santa Cruz Banana Slugs en.wikipedia.org/wiki/UC_Santa_Cruz_Banana_Slugs.

Chapter 9: Tribes & Tipping Points

1. Schultz, Cialdini (2007). *The constructive, destructive and reconstructive power of social norms.* Psychological Science.

2. Aronson & Leary (1982-83). *The relative effectiveness of models and prompts on energy conservation: A field experiment in a shower room.* Journal of Environmental Systems.

3. Goldstien, Griskevicus, & Cialdini (2007). *Invoking social norms: A social psychology perspective on improving hotel's linen reuse programs.* Cornell Hotel and Restaurant Administration Quarterly.

4. Christakis & Fowler (2007). *The Spread of Obesity in a Large Social Network over 32 Years.* The New England Journal of Medicine.

5. Rogers, Everett M. *Diffusion of Innovations,* New York, Free Press, 2005.

6. Wikipedia, *Phase-out of lightweight plastic bags* wikipedia.org/wiki/Phase-out_of_lightweight_plastic_bags

7. Gladwell (2000). *The Tipping Point,* New York.

Aaron Cassar	Carole Rey	Holden Bonwit	Lara Harland	Rebecca McDowell
Abel Thomas	Caroline Pidcock	Ian Fletcher	Les	Rebecca Webber
Adam Lerman	Cary Norsworthy	Ibrahim Ayub	Lisa Tracy	Regina Walton
Adrian Lu	Cecilia Macaulay	Ileana Betancourt	Lisa Wininger	Rob Hart
Adrian Ye	Ches Hall	Irene Schlatter	Lucia Jombikova	Rosie Wrede
Alan Fletcher	Christopher Philipp	Ivan Ovechkin	Luke Dokter	Roy Simkes
Alex Glow	Claire Morgan	Jack Lenox	Madeleine Wollin	Ruo-Mei Chua
Alex Machacek	Dan Stokols	Jacob Marshal Hale	Marc Roth	Ruth Andrade
Alexandra Marks	Dan White	James Moreda	Marion Rose	Sadie
Alison Westwood	Daniel Enking	Janee Taylor	Mary C Eggert	Sarah O'Sell
Amanda Lamont	David Kurtz	Jason Coleman	Matt Lehrman	Sean Marsh
Amanda Little	David Lowenfels	J Bowen	Matt Wilson Plasek	Selena Griffith
Amanda Powtir	David Parry	Jennifer Maverick	Matt Rutherford	Shafiq Ahmed
Amy Cocodis	David A Hood	Jeremy Mansfield	Max Nepstad	Shelly Miller
Andrea Minano	Derek Louden	Jillian Stahl	Maya Zuckerman	Stephanie
Andrew Butler	Donncha Foley	Joana Ribeiro	Melissa Keys	Hernandez
Andrew Corney	Duleesha Kulasooriya	Joanne Dawkins	Merce Labordena	Stefanie O'Brien
Andrew Louis Ostrom	Edward Reed	John R. Harrington	Michael Estigoy	Tamara
Andrew Murray	Eleonore Stureborg	Johnicholas Hines	Mike Lehenbauer	Tero Satomaa
Angelo Yazar	Emiliano Amaro	John Amos	Mo Rahman	Tim Jones
Anna Novikova	Emily Parvanae	Jon Dee	Nada Lopes	Tito Jankowski

Thank You Everyone!

Thank you to everyone who supported the Indiegogo
campaign and helped make this book possible.

Anouk Dijkman	Emma Adkisson	Jonathan Jutsen	Nanz Nair	Todd Houstein
Ashley Curtis	Erin Rhoads	Jordan J.	Natalie Zandt	Tom Bishop
Bill Gray	Esther Bailey	Jordan Daniels	Nick Aster	Tom Kabat
Beatrice Dauphinais	Eva Rottenanger	Joseph Nied	Nick Helweg-Larsen	Tom Malone
Bjorn Bertoft	Felix MacNeill	Josh Samuels	Olya Irzak	Tomas Declercq
Bobby Fishkin	Fiona Waterhouse	Joy Langley	Pablo Virgo	Veslemøy Klavenes-
Brandon Hall	Gabriel Pickard	Kate Lee	Paolo Mazzi	Berge
Brayden McLean	Gary Ellett	Katelyn Lyster	Paul McCarthy	Vashi Devat
Brent Dixon	Georgina Cronshaw	Katherine Lustig	Peter Dowson	Wes White
Brian Falldin	George Mingin	Katheryn	Pierre-Alexis	William Fitzgerald
Bridget Gardner	Gillian Butler	Leopoldseder	Ciavaldini	Zach Weismann
Brittany Bennett	Gordon Young	Kathryn Neville	Pip Marks	Zoey Cseresznyes
Brooke Webster	Graham Freeman	Kathleen Moynahan	Puck Algera	
Bushra Faiz	Greg Campbell	Kathleen Trisdale	Quentin Grimaud	
Cameron Burgess	Greg Martin	Kevin Jones	Raymond McCauley	
Carissa Fischer	Heide Hackworth	Kirstin Hunter	Reade Smith	

AUTHOR BIO

Katie Patrick is an Australian-American environmental engineer and software designer. Her company, *Hello World Labs,* applies data-driven, game design, and behavior-change techniques to solve the world's most pressing environmental problems. She is the creator of the zero waste behavior-change game, Youtube series, and book *Detrashed*. Katie is the founder of *Zerowastify.com,* an app designed to better measure and report municipal solid waste, and *UrbanCanopy.io,* a map-based application that uses spectral imaging of urban heat islands and vegetation cover to encourage urban greening initiatives.

Katie has been a media spokesperson on environmental issues and has been featured regularly on TV, radio and in magazines including the *BBC, Vogue Australia,* and *ABC.* She was CEO of the VC-funded green-lifestyle magazine *Green Pages Australia* and was appointed environmental brand ambassador by the Ogilvy Earth advertising agency for Volkswagen, Lipton Tea, and Wolfblass Wines.

She has served on the board of Australia's national eco-label, *Good Environmental Choice Australia,* and won the 2008 *Cosmopolitan Woman of the Year Award* for entrepreneurship. After graduating from the Royal Melbourne Institute of Technology with a B.Eng in Environmental Engineering, she worked as an environmental design engineer for building engineers Lincoln Scott in Sydney Australia on some of the world's first platinum-LEED-certified commercial buildings. Katie lives in San Francisco with her young daughter Anastasia.

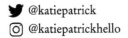 @katiepatrick
@katiepatrickhello

CPSIA information can be obtained
at www.ICGtesting.com
Printed in the USA
LVHW070319050919
630003LV00015B/59/P